STAR WARS

FOLDED FLYERS

BY BENJAMIN HARPER AND
THE SCIENTISTS OF KLUTZ LABS

KLUTZ

KLUTZ® creates activity books and other great stuff for kids ages 3 to 103. We began our corporate life in 1977 in a garage we shared with a Chevrolet Impala. Although we've outgrown that first office, Klutz galactic headquarters remains in Palo Alto, California, and we're still staffed entirely by real human beings. For those of you who collect mission statements, here's ours:

• CREATE WONDERFUL THINGS • BE GOOD • HAVE FUN

WRITE US:

We would love to hear your comments regarding this or any of our books. We have many!

KLUTZ®

450 Lambert Avenue
Palo Alto, CA 94306

VISIT OUR WEBSITE:

You can check out all the stuff we make, find a nearby retailer, request a catalog, sign up for a newsletter, e-mail us, or just goof off!

www.klutz.com

Book printed in Korea. 91

Distributed in Canada by Scholastic Canada Ltd
604 King Street West, Toronto, Ontario, Canada M5V 1E1

Distributed in the UK by Scholastic UK Ltd
Westfield Road, Southam, Warwickshire, England CV47 0RA

Distributed in Australia by Scholastic Australia Ltd
PO Box 579, Gosford, NSW, Australia 2250

VISIT THE OFFICIAL STAR WARS WEBSITE:
www.starwars.com

CONTENTS

THE STARFIGHTERS

FEATURING:

USE THE FLIGHT-TESTED, READY-TO-FOLD PAPER AND TAPE IN THE BACK OF THE BOOK TO MAKE 5 OF EACH STARFIGHTER.

A BEGINNER'S GUIDE TO STARFIGHTERS

WHAT'S A STARFIGHTER?

A starfighter is a small spaceship designed to attack at incredible speeds, outmaneuver its enemies, and protect larger and slower spacecraft.

Generally, these small ships have room for only one pilot. To make the pilot's job easier, these ships have an onboard astromech droid — such as R2-D2 or R4-P17. Astromech droids help make general repairs, program weapons, calculate hyperspace travel routes, and navigate the ship.

Many starfighters are equipped with hyperdrive engines. These engines blast ships into hyperspace, where they can travel enormous distances in seconds. Many starfighters are also equipped with laser cannons, ion cannons, and proton torpedo launchers.

YOUR FOLDED STARFIGHTERS

With this book, you get specially printed paper from which you can fold six different functional starfighters. The scientists of Klutz Labs designed these foldable fighters for easy folding and amazing flying.

You won't need an onboard droid to help you fly these folded starfighters. Just consult the pilot's manual at the end of each set of folding instructions for flying tips, and you'll be ready to blast off.

Unfortunately, Klutz Labs was not able to equip these starfighters with hyperdrive engines, laser cannons, or proton torpedo launchers. Folded paper is simply not able to withstand the forces involved.

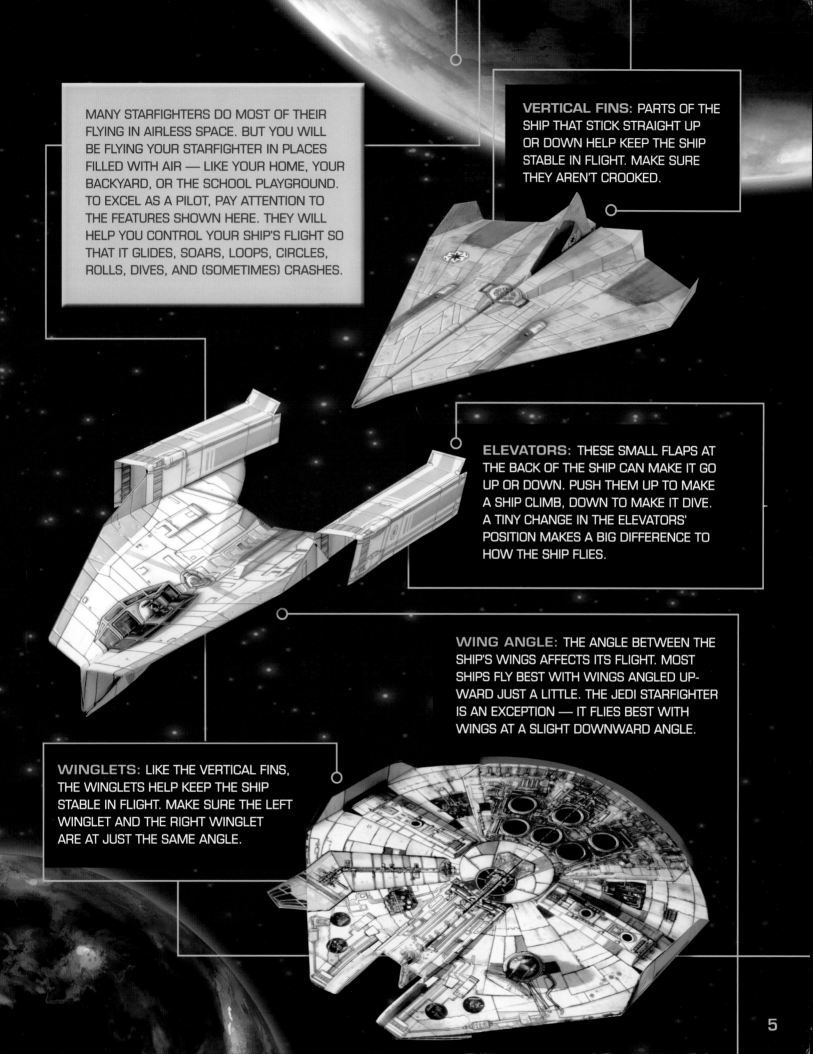

MANY STARFIGHTERS DO MOST OF THEIR FLYING IN AIRLESS SPACE. BUT YOU WILL BE FLYING YOUR STARFIGHTER IN PLACES FILLED WITH AIR — LIKE YOUR HOME, YOUR BACKYARD, OR THE SCHOOL PLAYGROUND. TO EXCEL AS A PILOT, PAY ATTENTION TO THE FEATURES SHOWN HERE. THEY WILL HELP YOU CONTROL YOUR SHIP'S FLIGHT SO THAT IT GLIDES, SOARS, LOOPS, CIRCLES, ROLLS, DIVES, AND (SOMETIMES) CRASHES.

VERTICAL FINS: PARTS OF THE SHIP THAT STICK STRAIGHT UP OR DOWN HELP KEEP THE SHIP STABLE IN FLIGHT. MAKE SURE THEY AREN'T CROOKED.

ELEVATORS: THESE SMALL FLAPS AT THE BACK OF THE SHIP CAN MAKE IT GO UP OR DOWN. PUSH THEM UP TO MAKE A SHIP CLIMB, DOWN TO MAKE IT DIVE. A TINY CHANGE IN THE ELEVATORS' POSITION MAKES A BIG DIFFERENCE TO HOW THE SHIP FLIES.

WING ANGLE: THE ANGLE BETWEEN THE SHIP'S WINGS AFFECTS ITS FLIGHT. MOST SHIPS FLY BEST WITH WINGS ANGLED UP-WARD JUST A LITTLE. THE JEDI STARFIGHTER IS AN EXCEPTION — IT FLIES BEST WITH WINGS AT A SLIGHT DOWNWARD ANGLE.

WINGLETS: LIKE THE VERTICAL FINS, THE WINGLETS HELP KEEP THE SHIP STABLE IN FLIGHT. MAKE SURE THE LEFT WINGLET AND THE RIGHT WINGLET ARE AT JUST THE SAME ANGLE.

SLOPPY FOLDS MAKE SLOPPY STARFIGHTERS.
SLOPPY STARFIGHTERS DON'T FLY WELL.
IN A TOP-NOTCH STARFIGHTER, ALL FOLDS ARE SHARP
AND EXACT. HERE'S HOW TO MAKE A PERFECT FOLD.

READ THIS YOU MUST

1 // CHECK THE PICTURE

Do you have the right piece of paper? Is the right side up?

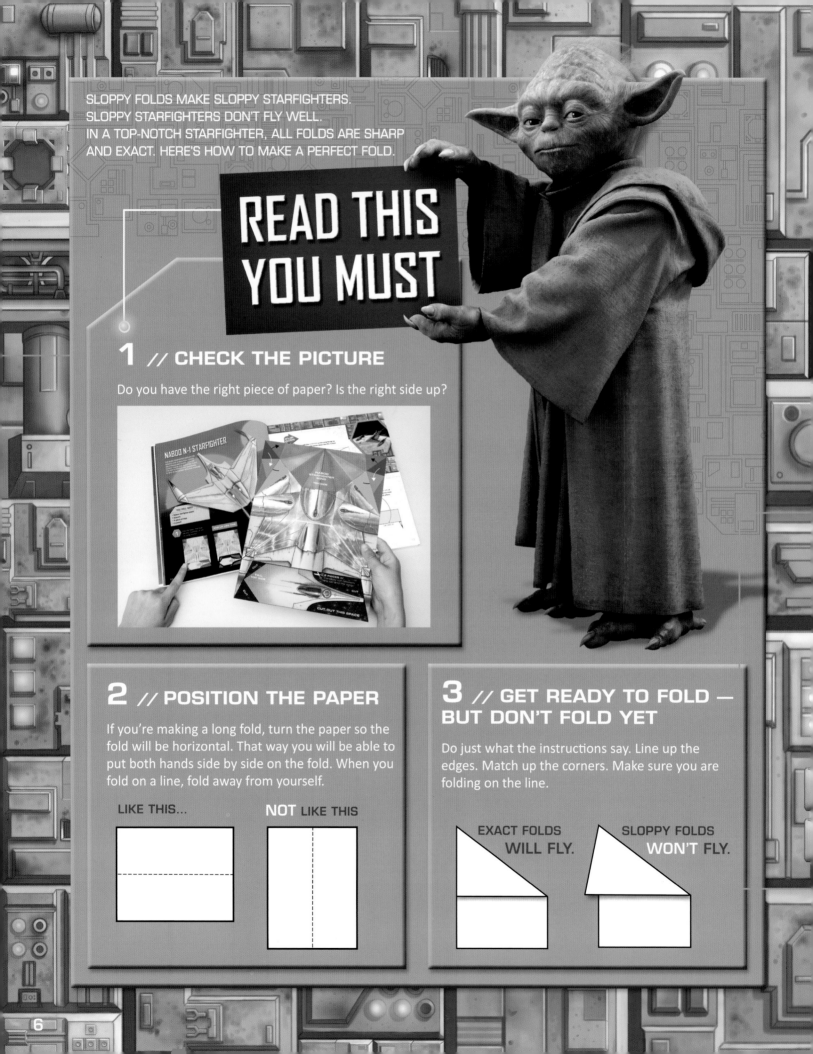

2 // POSITION THE PAPER

If you're making a long fold, turn the paper so the fold will be horizontal. That way you will be able to put both hands side by side on the fold. When you fold on a line, fold away from yourself.

LIKE THIS...   **NOT** LIKE THIS

3 // GET READY TO FOLD — BUT DON'T FOLD YET

Do just what the instructions say. Line up the edges. Match up the corners. Make sure you are folding on the line.

EXACT FOLDS   SLOPPY FOLDS
WILL FLY.   WON'T FLY.

4 // FOLD

Push a finger down on the middle of the fold, make sure you are folding in the right spot, and then smooth the paper down in both directions from the middle.

5 // CREASE WELL

Run your fingernail along the fold to make a sharp crease. When you're folding many layers, your fingernail may not be enough. Run the edge of a ruler over the fold to flatten the layers.

PERFECT!

USE PAPER FROM THE BACK OF THE BOOK. THE MARKS ON THE PAPER WILL HELP YOU FOLD A PERFECT SHIP.

Dashed lines show where to fold.

– – – – – – – – – – – – – – –

When you can make a fold by matching up the edges or the corners, you don't need a fold line. So the paper won't have one.

Blue lines and areas filled with outer space show where to cut. Blue squares show where to stop cutting.

This tells you when to flip the paper over.

FLIP OVER

FLIGHT SCHOOL

ASK ANY SHIPBUILDER HOW MANY OF THEIR SHIPS FLEW PERFECTLY ON THE FIRST TIME OUT. YOU MAY GET A DIRTY LOOK FOR AN ANSWER.

WHETHER THEY ARE FOLDED FROM PAPER OR BUILT OF TITANIUM, MOST STARFIGHTERS NEED A FEW ADJUSTMENTS TO FLY RIGHT.

CHECK FOR SYMMETRY

That's a fancy way to say that the left side looks like a mirror image of the right. If the left wing is different from the right, your ship won't fly straight (if it flies at all). If you make a mistake on one side of your ship, try to make the exact same mistake on the other side.

All the ships in this book have symmetry — except for the *Millennium Falcon*. Like its pilot, Han Solo, the *Millennium Falcon* breaks a lot of rules. This ship has a cockpit sticking out one side. That cockpit makes the ship fly in circles — but it still flies great.

THIS SHIP FLIES.
Only the cockpit breaks the symmetry.

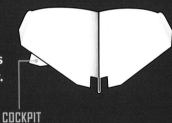

COCKPIT

THIS PLANE CRASHES.
All sorts of things are out of whack.

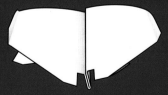

THROW, CHECK, TWEAK

To get your ship to fly right, you need to experiment. The process goes sort of like this:

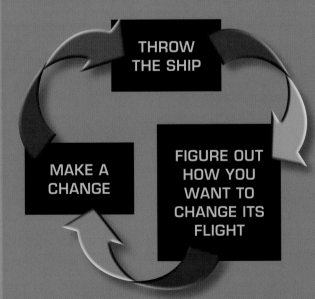

THROW THE SHIP

FIGURE OUT HOW YOU WANT TO CHANGE ITS FLIGHT

MAKE A CHANGE

SUPER SECRET TIP:
READ THE PILOT'S MANUAL

To get the best flight from a ship, read the instructions for that starfighter. Try to fly a Y-wing like a TIE Advanced, and you'll be very disappointed.

AFTER EVERY CRASH

Straighten any crooked bits.
Check for symmetry.

REPAIR DOCK

PROBLEM //
MY SHIP ROLLS OVER AND FLIES UPSIDE DOWN

// CHANGE
LIFT THE WINGS SO THEY MAKE A V-SHAPE.

PROBLEM //
MY SHIP DIVES FOR THE GROUND

// CHANGE
PUSH THE ELEVATORS UP A LITTLE.

PROBLEM //
MY SHIP TURNS OR BARREL ROLLS

// CHANGE
CHECK FOR SYMMETRY.

PROBLEM //
MY SHIP CLIMBS STEEPLY, THEN CRASHES

// CHANGE
PUSH THE ELEVATORS DOWN A LITTLE OR EASE UP ON YOUR THROW.

PROBLEM //
MY SHIP JUST DOESN'T FLY RIGHT

// CHANGE
MAKE SURE THE FOLD AT THE FRONT EDGE IS SHARP. IF ALL ELSE FAILS, FOLD A NEW SHIP.

NABOO N-1 STARFIGHTER

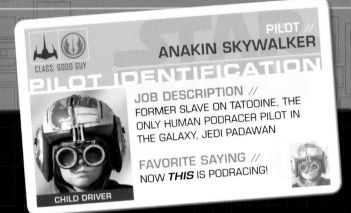

PILOT //
ANAKIN SKYWALKER

CLASS: GOOD GUY

PILOT IDENTIFICATION

JOB DESCRIPTION //
FORMER SLAVE ON TATOOINE, THE
ONLY HUMAN PODRACER PILOT IN
THE GALAXY, JEDI PADAWAN

FAVORITE SAYING //
NOW **THIS** IS PODRACING!

CHILD DRIVER

CENTRAL RAT-TAIL
ACTS AS POWERCHARGER

SHIP'S COMPUTER
SYSTEMS INTERACT WITH
ONBOARD R2 UNIT

WINDSHIELD
SLIDES FORWARD

TRADITIONAL
CHROMIUM FINISH

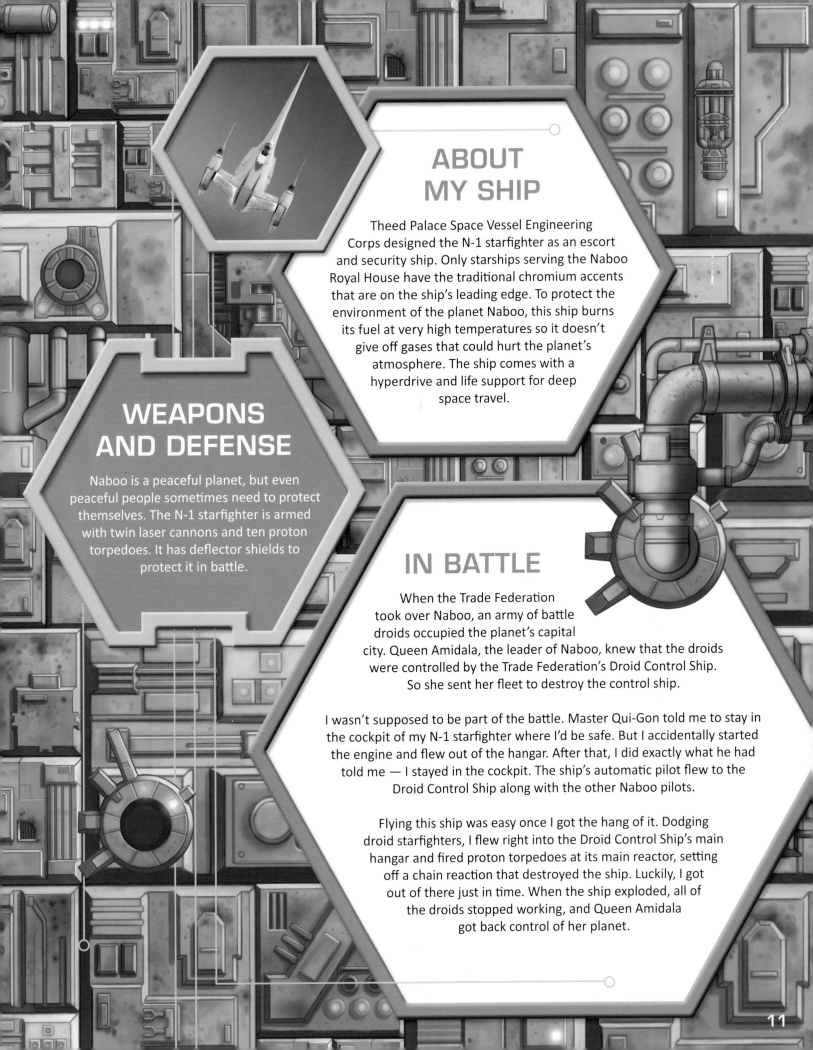

ABOUT MY SHIP

Theed Palace Space Vessel Engineering Corps designed the N-1 starfighter as an escort and security ship. Only starships serving the Naboo Royal House have the traditional chromium accents that are on the ship's leading edge. To protect the environment of the planet Naboo, this ship burns its fuel at very high temperatures so it doesn't give off gases that could hurt the planet's atmosphere. The ship comes with a hyperdrive and life support for deep space travel.

WEAPONS AND DEFENSE

Naboo is a peaceful planet, but even peaceful people sometimes need to protect themselves. The N-1 starfighter is armed with twin laser cannons and ten proton torpedoes. It has deflector shields to protect it in battle.

IN BATTLE

When the Trade Federation took over Naboo, an army of battle droids occupied the planet's capital city. Queen Amidala, the leader of Naboo, knew that the droids were controlled by the Trade Federation's Droid Control Ship. So she sent her fleet to destroy the control ship.

I wasn't supposed to be part of the battle. Master Qui-Gon told me to stay in the cockpit of my N-1 starfighter where I'd be safe. But I accidentally started the engine and flew out of the hangar. After that, I did exactly what he had told me — I stayed in the cockpit. The ship's automatic pilot flew to the Droid Control Ship along with the other Naboo pilots.

Flying this ship was easy once I got the hang of it. Dodging droid starfighters, I flew right into the Droid Control Ship's main hangar and fired proton torpedoes at its main reactor, setting off a chain reaction that destroyed the ship. Luckily, I got out of there just in time. When the ship exploded, all of the droids stopped working, and Queen Amidala got back control of her planet.

NABOO N-1 STARFIGHTER

THIS SLEEK STARFIGHTER DISPLAYS THE NABOO'S LOVE OF BEAUTIFUL CURVES AND STREAMLINED SHAPES. WITH ITS ELEGANT DESIGN AND SWOOPING FLIGHT, THIS SHIP IS PERFECT FOR CEREMONIAL FLY-BYS OR IMPORTANT SCOUTING MISSIONS.

YOU WILL NEED:

- Naboo starfighter paper
- Scissors
- A piece of tape
- A pencil

1 Find the paper that looks like this. Carefully cut out the wing and tail.

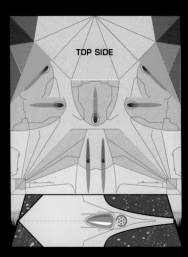

TOP SIDE

END UP LIKE THIS

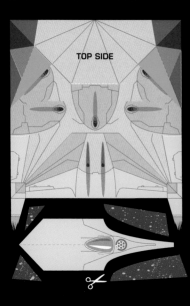

TOP SIDE

FLIP OVER

2 Start with the **underside** of the wing facing up. Fold the top right corner down like this. Crease well and unfold.

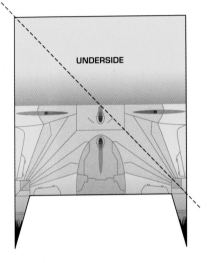

UNDERSIDE

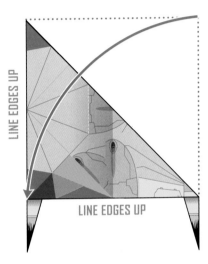

LINE EDGES UP

LINE EDGES UP

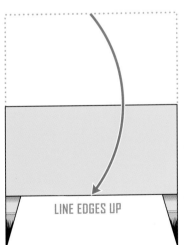

FLIP OVER

3 Repeat step 2 with the top left corner. Crease well and unfold.

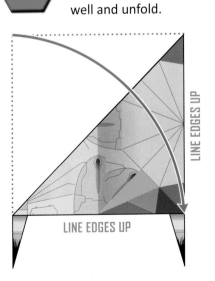

LINE EDGES UP

LINE EDGES UP

4 Lay the paper on a flat surface with the **top side** of the wing facing up. Fold the top edge down to meet the straight edge you cut. Crease well and unfold.

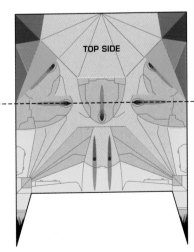

TOP SIDE

LINE EDGES UP

13

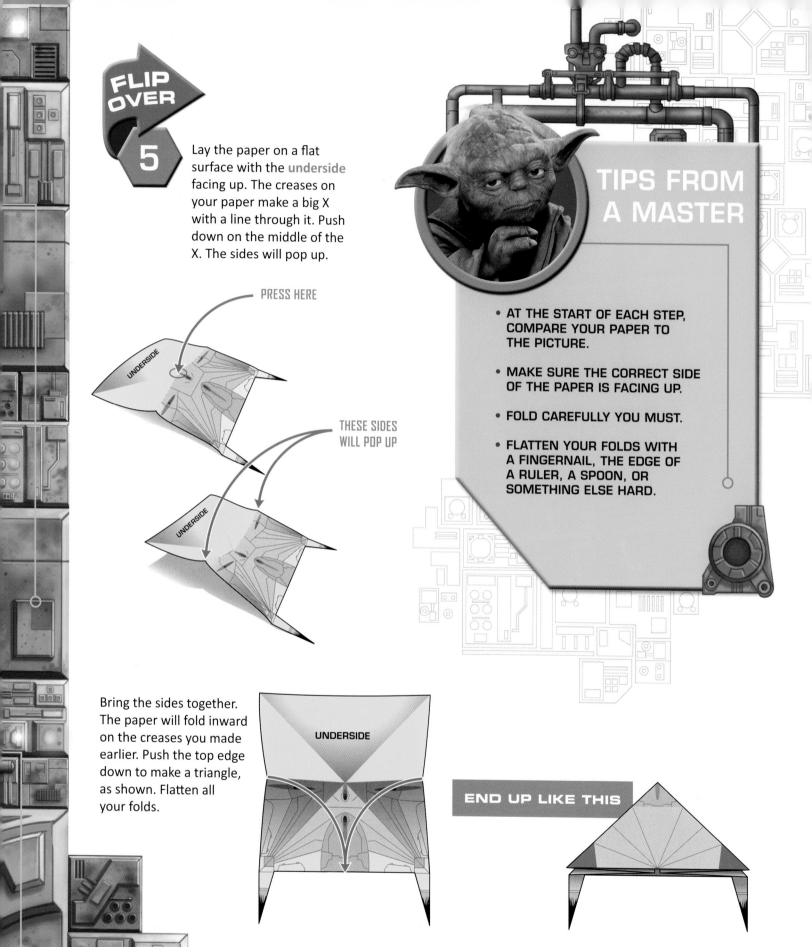

FLIP OVER

5

Lay the paper on a flat surface with the underside facing up. The creases on your paper make a big X with a line through it. Push down on the middle of the X. The sides will pop up.

PRESS HERE

UNDERSIDE

THESE SIDES WILL POP UP

UNDERSIDE

TIPS FROM A MASTER

- AT THE START OF EACH STEP, COMPARE YOUR PAPER TO THE PICTURE.

- MAKE SURE THE CORRECT SIDE OF THE PAPER IS FACING UP.

- FOLD CAREFULLY YOU MUST.

- FLATTEN YOUR FOLDS WITH A FINGERNAIL, THE EDGE OF A RULER, A SPOON, OR SOMETHING ELSE HARD.

Bring the sides together. The paper will fold inward on the creases you made earlier. Push the top edge down to make a triangle, as shown. Flatten all your folds.

UNDERSIDE

END UP LIKE THIS

6 Grab one of the red points of the big triangle. Fold that corner to the top corner of the triangle. Then do the same with the other red point.

END UP LIKE THIS

7 Fold each dark purple triangle so it lands exactly on top of the light purple triangle.

END UP LIKE THIS

8 Fold each lime green triangle so it lands on the red triangle. Flatten your folds.

END UP LIKE THIS

NOW UNFOLD THE FOLDS YOU JUST MADE IN STEP 8.

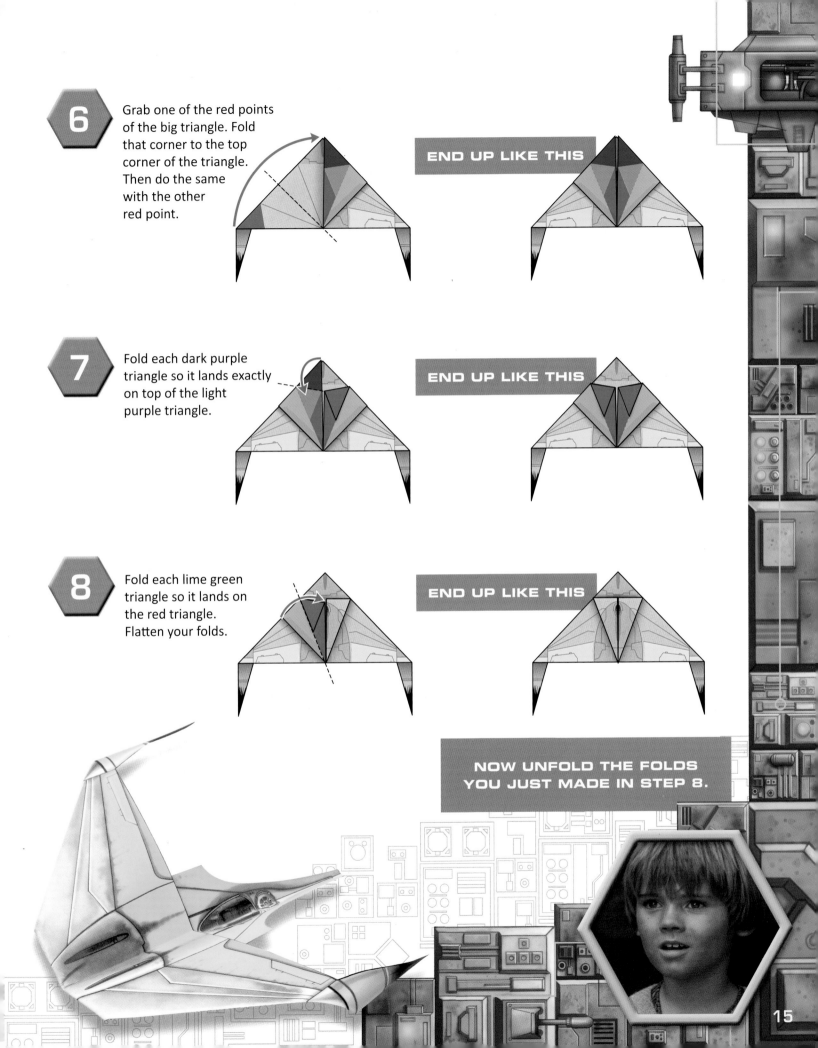

9 Fold the tail in half, length-wise. Crease and unfold.

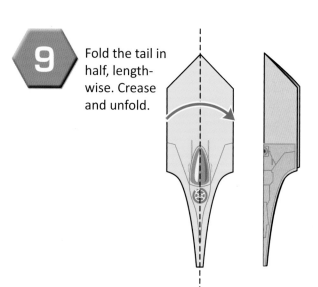

10 Place the tail and the wing on a flat surface with the **undersides** facing up. If you forgot to unfold after step 8, do it now. Slide the fat end of the tail between the top and bottom layers of the wing, up to the purple line.

PUSH IN TO PURPLE LINE

11 Fold the triangle at the top of the wing down. This fold will hold the tail in place.

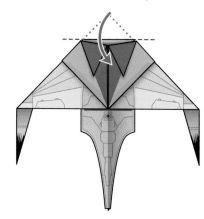

12 Here's the trickiest step. The triangle from step 11 has two pockets. Repeat step 8 — but this time slide the corner that you fold up into the pocket of the triangle as shown. Flatten all the folds well.

END UP LIKE THIS

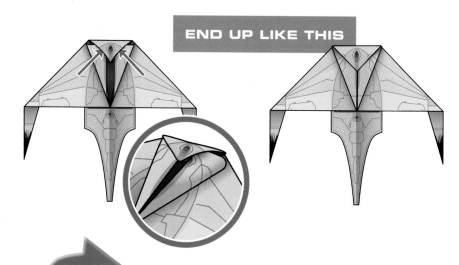

FLIP OVER

13 Make sure the tail is right in the middle of the wing. Add a piece of tape to hold the tail in place.

TAPE HERE

FLIP OVER

14 Place the wing on a flat surface with the **underside** facing up. Lay a pencil on a tip of the wing like this. Roll the wing tip around the pencil once, then release the paper. You want the sweeping points of the wing to form half-tubes. Repeat for both sides. (Don't skip this step. Those tubes really help the ship fly.)

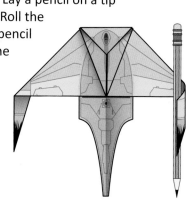

15 Gently fold the ship in half. Do not crease the center fold. Unfold.

NOW YOU'RE
READY TO FLY

PILOT'S MANUAL //
NABOO STARFIGHTER

THIS SHIP LIKES TO CIRCLE AND SWOOP. HOLD IT BY PINCHING THE TRIANGLE ON THE BOTTOM OF THE SHIP. THROW IT UPWARD AS HARD AS YOU CAN.

IF YOUR SHIP DOESN'T FLY RIGHT ON YOUR FIRST TOSS:

- Run the front edge of the ship between your finger and thumb to make sure you have a sharp fold.

- Check to make sure that the left half of the ship is a mirror image of the right half.

- Double-check the curl of your wing tips — that can make a big difference.

YOU CAN ALSO GRAB THE NOSE OF THE NABOO STARFIGHTER AND FLING IT STRAIGHT UP. IF YOU GIVE THIS SHIP ENOUGH ALTITUDE, IT WILL HAVE THE SPACE IT NEEDS TO SWOOP AND THEN LEVEL OUT.

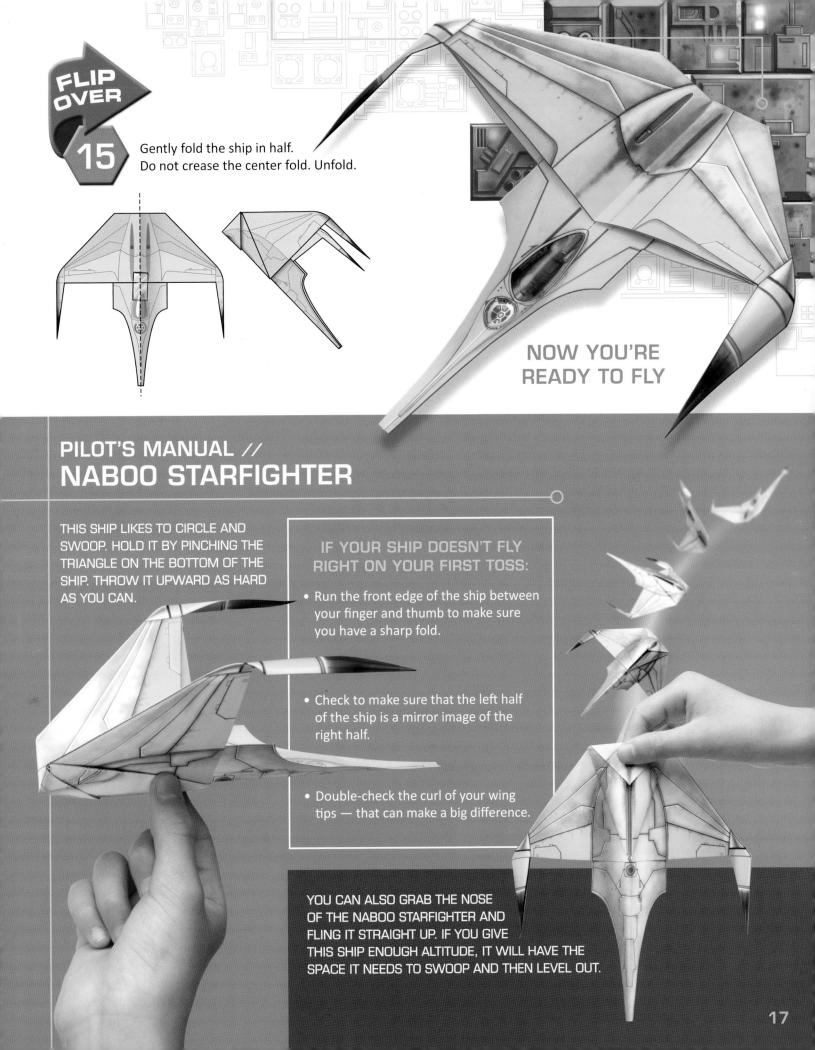

17

JEDI STARFIGHTER

SHIELD GENERATOR
AT REAR OF SHIP

WINDSHIELD IS
HINGED AT FRONT

LASER CANNONS

ASTROMECH DROID
HELPS ON MISSIONS

COMMUNICATIONS
TRANSCEIVER AT
FRONT OF SHIP SENDS
ENCRYPTED MESSAGES

ABOUT MY SHIP

The tiny Delta-7B *Aethersprite*-class light interceptor (also known as the Jedi starfighter) is the ship of choice for the Jedi. Kuat Systems Engineering designed it to be fast in battle and small enough to evade enemy fighters. It's so small that it can't house its own hyperdrive engine. To fly into hyperspace, the Jedi starfighter docks into a hyperspace ring, which transports the ship to its destination. The ship is also too small for a regular R2 unit to fly with it. An astromech droid must be hardwired into the ship.

WEAPONS AND DEFENSE

Each Jedi starfighter comes equipped with two dual laser cannons and a state of the art targeting system. Jedi reflexes make this ship a deadly foe. The ship has life support for up to five hours' worth of normal space travel. If the pilot goes into a Jedi trance, the air supply can last much longer.

IN BATTLE

After I battled Jango Fett on Kamino, he blasted off into space. He didn't know I had placed a tracer on his ship. I tracked him to Geonosis, a planet surrounded by a deadly asteroid ring. He picked up my ship on his sensors and launched an attack — with seismic charges, and then lasers, and finally a heat-seeking missile! To evade that missile, I had to dodge through the asteroid belt, twisting and turning around spinning space rocks. My astromech and I worked fast, jettisoning refuse. The missile hit the garbage instead of my ship and I was safe.

My former Padawan Anakin Skywalker is more adventurous in flying his Jedi starfighter. In the Battle of Bothawui, Anakin launched an attack against General Grievous's Separatist fleet in the middle of another asteroid belt. Anakin took on one of Grievous's battleships himself, evading all enemy fire, and blasted the ship's helm.

JEDI STARFIGHTER

THIS HIGH-PERFORMANCE STARFIGHTER WITH
POWERFUL ENGINES IS JUST WHAT YOU NEED
FOR ANY DANGEROUS MISSION. IT'S GREAT FOR
AN ENCOUNTER WITH PIRATES — OR FOR
FLYING LOOPS IN YOUR BACKYARD.

OBI-WAN KENOBI'S
STARFIGHTER

ANAKIN SKYWALKER'S
STARFIGHTER

YOU WILL NEED:

- Jedi starfighter paper — either yellow
  (Anakin's) or red (Obi-Wan Kenobi's)
- Scissors
- A piece of tape

1 We folded a yellow Jedi starfighter,
but you can use either yellow or
red. Cut off the two corners that
are filled with space (darkness
and stars, that is).

END UP LIKE THIS

TOP SIDE

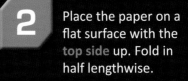

TOP SIDE

2 Place the paper on a
flat surface with the
top side up. Fold in
half lengthwise.

TOP SIDE

3 Find the blue triangle. Fold on the black dashed line that runs beside the triangle. Crease. Fold the other way. Unfold.

4 Unfold all the folds. Put the paper on a flat surface with the **underside** facing up. Fold the upper right corner down so the top edge matches up with the center crease. Do the same with the upper left corner.

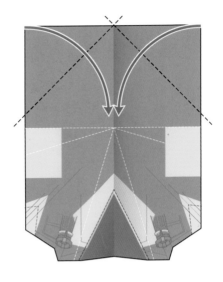 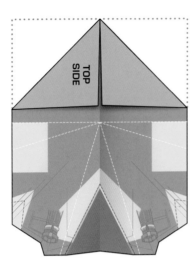

5 Fold the top point down. Fold exactly on the dashed purple line. Make sure the point lands right on the center crease.

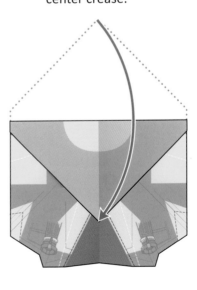

6 Fold the upper right corner down so the top fold matches up with the center crease. Do the same with the upper left corner.

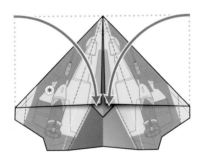

7 Find the little triangle that peeks out from under the corners you just folded down. Fold this triangle up.

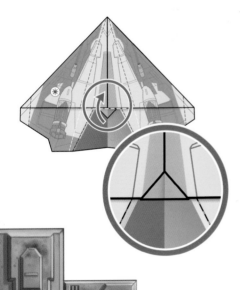

FLIP OVER

8 Flip the ship over. Fold in half along the center crease.

9 Fold the wing down on the dashed purple line.

IF YOU ARE AN EXPERT FOLDER, PAY ATTENTION TO THE TOP OF THE SHIP AS YOU FOLD. YOUR FOLD SHOULD RUN RIGHT THROUGH THE CIRCLE OF THE ASTROMECH'S HEAD.

FLIP OVER

10 Fold the second wing down so it lines up with the first wing. If you have to ignore the line to match the wings, that's ok.

11 Hold the ship by the nose and let the wings flatten out, spreading away from each other. Push up on the center of the blue triangle until it turns inside out and pops up.

THE SHIP WILL LOOK LIKE THIS FROM THE SIDE

12 Push the wings together so the ship looks like this. Add a piece of tape on the top.

TAPE HERE

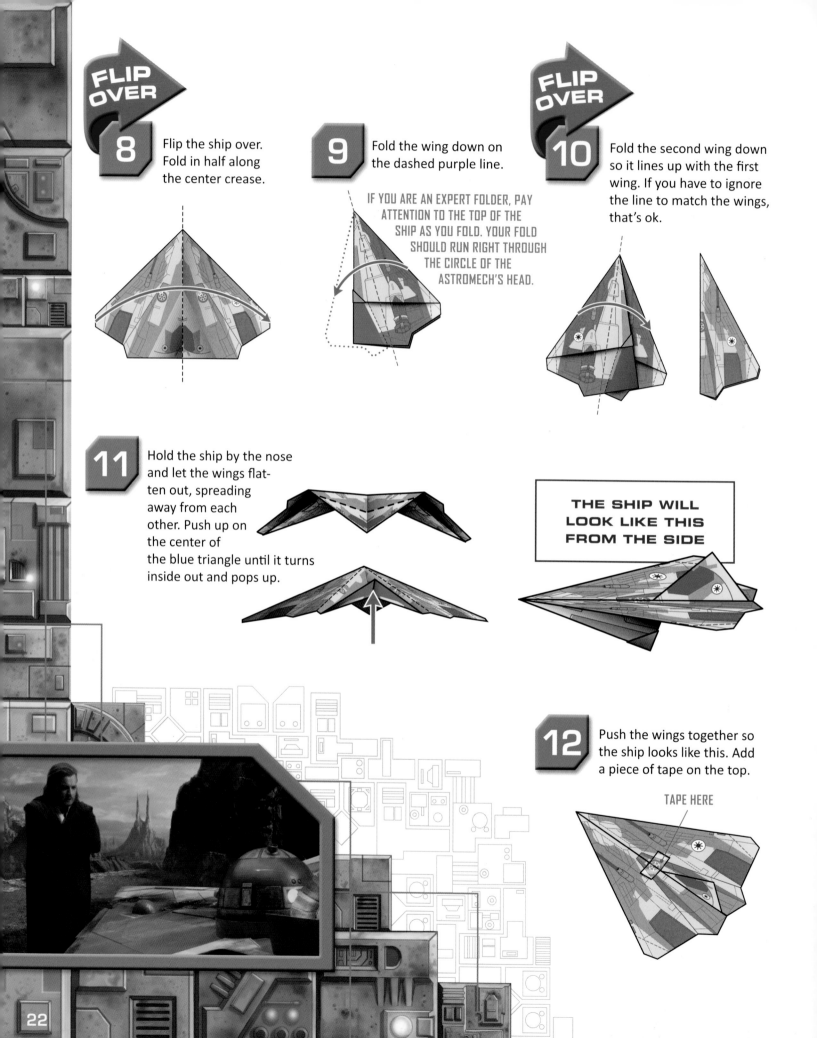

13 Flatten the ship on its side with the wings down. Fold up the winglet on the dashed purple line. Turn the ship over and fold up the winglet on the other wing.

14 At the back of the ship are two pointy elevator flaps. Bend them up just a little bit. Push the wings down so they slope downward from the center, just a bit.

BEND THE PAPER UNTIL THE SHIP LOOKS LIKE THIS FROM THE BACK

WINGLET FOLDED UP

WINGLET

SLIGHT BEND IN ELEVATORS

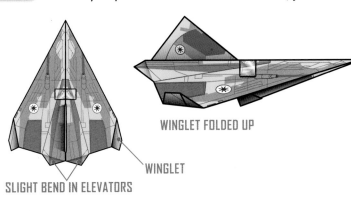

PILOT'S MANUAL //
JEDI STARFIGHTER

WANT A FLYER THAT CIRCLES AND LOOPS THE LOOP? THIS IS THE SHIP FOR YOU. IT NEEDS SPACE TO LOOP, SO FLY IT ON A PLAYGROUND OR IN A BIG ROOM WITH A HIGH CEILING.

TO MAKE THE SHIP FLY IN A LOOP, BEND THE ELEVATORS UP, POINT THE NOSE UP, AND THROW THE SHIP HARD. IF YOU DON'T HAVE SPACE TO LOOP, TOSS THE PLANE MEDIUM HARD FOR A GLIDING FLIGHT.

IF YOUR SHIP DOESN'T LOOP:

- Throw it harder.

- Push the elevators up a little.

- Make sure your ship looks like the one in step 14 — the wings slope downward; the cockpit is straight up; the winglets are folded up at an angle.

MILLENNIUM FALCON

QUAD LASER
CANNON

SENSOR DISH

DEFLECTOR SHIELD
GENERATOR

CONCUSSION MISSILE
TUBES

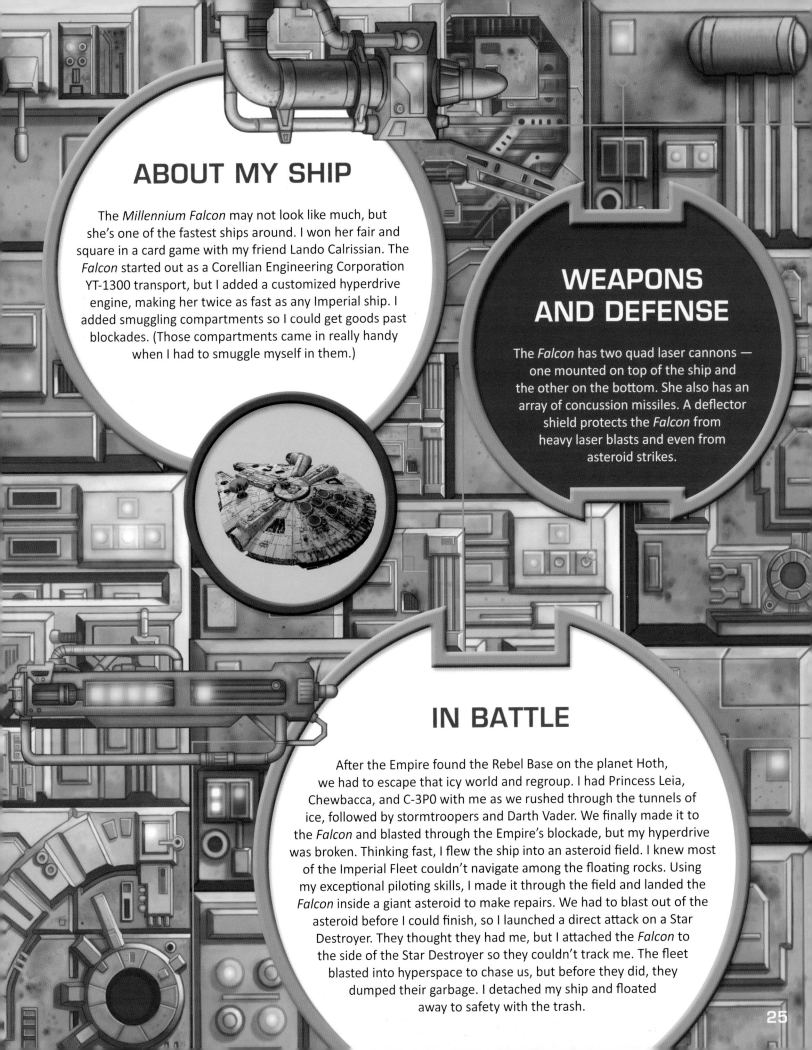

ABOUT MY SHIP

The *Millennium Falcon* may not look like much, but she's one of the fastest ships around. I won her fair and square in a card game with my friend Lando Calrissian. The *Falcon* started out as a Corellian Engineering Corporation YT-1300 transport, but I added a customized hyperdrive engine, making her twice as fast as any Imperial ship. I added smuggling compartments so I could get goods past blockades. (Those compartments came in really handy when I had to smuggle myself in them.)

WEAPONS AND DEFENSE

The *Falcon* has two quad laser cannons — one mounted on top of the ship and the other on the bottom. She also has an array of concussion missiles. A deflector shield protects the *Falcon* from heavy laser blasts and even from asteroid strikes.

IN BATTLE

After the Empire found the Rebel Base on the planet Hoth, we had to escape that icy world and regroup. I had Princess Leia, Chewbacca, and C-3PO with me as we rushed through the tunnels of ice, followed by stormtroopers and Darth Vader. We finally made it to the *Falcon* and blasted through the Empire's blockade, but my hyperdrive was broken. Thinking fast, I flew the ship into an asteroid field. I knew most of the Imperial Fleet couldn't navigate among the floating rocks. Using my exceptional piloting skills, I made it through the field and landed the *Falcon* inside a giant asteroid to make repairs. We had to blast out of the asteroid before I could finish, so I launched a direct attack on a Star Destroyer. They thought they had me, but I attached the *Falcon* to the side of the Star Destroyer so they couldn't track me. The fleet blasted into hyperspace to chase us, but before they did, they dumped their garbage. I detached my ship and floated away to safety with the trash.

MILLENNIUM FALCON

THE MILLENNIUM FALCON THAT HAN SOLO FLIES STARTED ITS LIFE AS A CORELLIAN FREIGHTER. YOUR MILLENNIUM FALCON STARTS AS A PIECE OF PAPER. BUT IN THE RIGHT HANDS (YOURS, PERHAPS?), YOUR FALCON COULD ALSO BECOME KNOWN THROUGHOUT THE GALAXY — OR AT LEAST AROUND YOUR SCHOOLYARD.

YOU WILL NEED:

- *Millennium Falcon* paper
- Scissors
- 4 pieces of tape

1 Find the paper that looks like this. Cut off the corners by cutting on the curved lines.

END UP LIKE THIS

FLIP OVER

2

With the **underside** facing up, fold the top edge down to the left edge to make a diagonal fold. Then unfold.

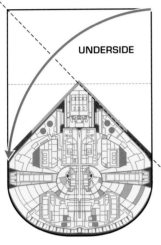

UNDERSIDE

LINE EDGES UP

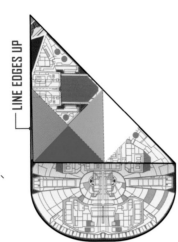

3

Do the same thing with the other corner. Fold, crease, and unfold.

LINE EDGES UP

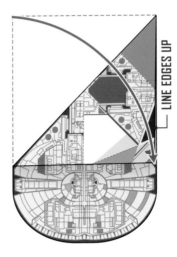

FLIP OVER

4

Make sure the **top side** faces up. The creases make a big X. Fold the top edge down on the dashed line to make a horizontal fold through the middle of the X. Line up the corners with the bottom of the X. Crease well and unfold.

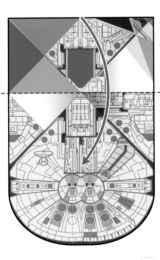

FLIP OVER

5

Lay the paper on a flat surface with the **underside** facing up. Push down on the middle of the X. The sides will pop up.

PRESS HERE

UNDERSIDE

THESE SIDES WILL POP UP

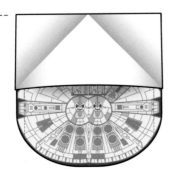

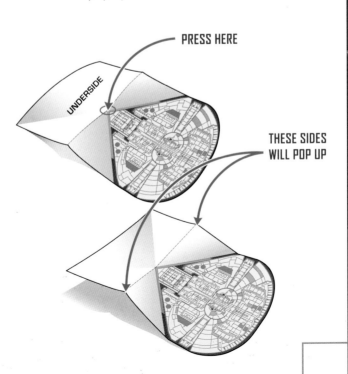

6 Bring the sides forward and together. The paper will fold inward on the creases of your X and the top will move down. Flatten all your folds.

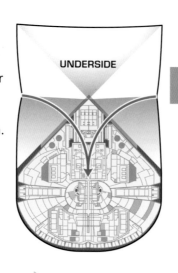

UNDERSIDE

END UP LIKE THIS

FLIP OVER

7 Fold the ship in half lengthwise. Crease well and unfold.

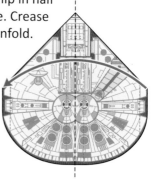

FLIP OVER

8 Grab the corner of the purple triangle on the right. Fold it to the left on the center fold.

9 Fold the turquoise triangle up on the dotted line so it covers the lime green triangle. Crease well.

10 Grab the tiny pink triangle on the left. Fold it to the right on the center fold.

FOLD OVER THE TOP LAYER ONLY

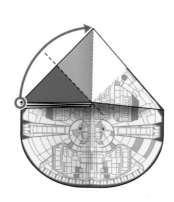

FOLD OVER THE TOP LAYER ONLY

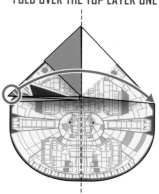

11 Making the ship's cockpit is tricky. First, fold the pink triangle up on the dashed line. Unfold it, then fold it the other way. Then unfold it again.

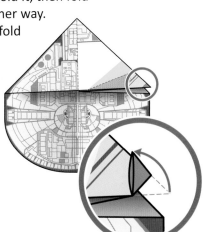

12 The pink triangle is at the tip of a big triangle made of two layers of paper. Pull the layers apart and tuck the pink triangle inside. When you're done, the pink triangle will be hidden.

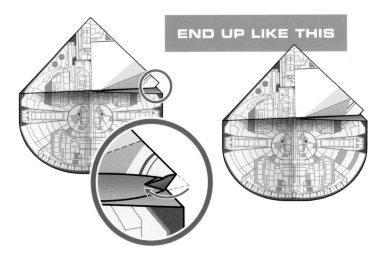

END UP LIKE THIS

13 Fold the orange triangle up on the dotted line so it covers the yellow triangle. Crease well.

END UP LIKE THIS

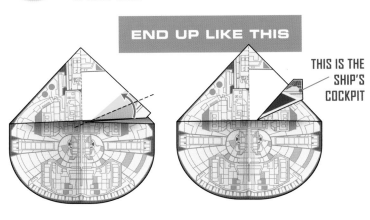

THIS IS THE SHIP'S COCKPIT

14 Fold the top layer, with the cockpit, to the left on the center crease. Add tape as shown.

END UP LIKE THIS

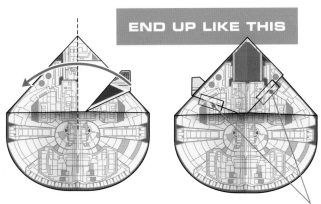

TAPE HERE AND HERE

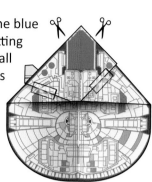

15 Cut on the blue lines, cutting through all the layers of paper.

16 Fold the red shape and the dark purple triangles down as shown. Be sure to fold down all the layers. Tape the purple triangles in place.

END UP LIKE THIS

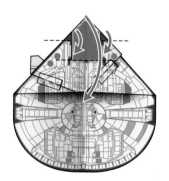

TAPE HERE AND HERE

FLIP OVER

17 Fold the ship in half along the fold you made before. Make sure your folded ship looks like this:

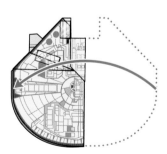

THIS PART IS HARD TO FOLD. GET HELP IF YOU NEED IT.

18 Fold the wing down on the dashed red line. You'll have to work hard to get the center to fold. No one said building a starfighter was easy.

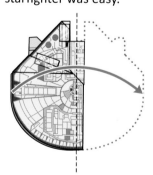

19 Fold the other wing down so it matches up with the first wing. Crease well.

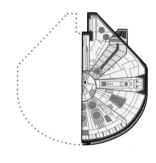

20 Open the wing. Fold each wing tip up on the purple dashed line. Be sure to do both sides.

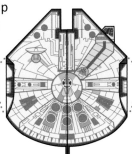

21 Unfold the wing tips.

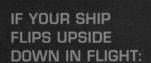

HERE'S WHAT THE SHIP
LOOKS LIKE FROM THE FRONT

22 Put a piece of tape on the nose to hold the two halves together.

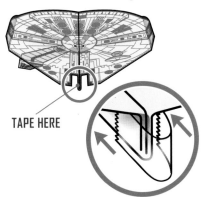

TAPE HERE

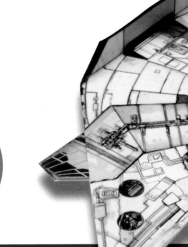

PILOT'S MANUAL //
MILLENNIUM FALCON

THE MILLENNIUM FALCON IS A GLIDER THAT TENDS TO CIRCLE AND SPIRAL. THROW IT LEVEL WITH A GENTLE TOSS.

IF YOUR SHIP WON'T FLY:

- Make sure the nose isn't bent up or down.

- Check the wings for curves. Flat wings fly best.

IF YOUR SHIP FLIPS UPSIDE DOWN IN FLIGHT:

- Congratulate yourself on your stunt-flying ability.

- If you'd rather fly right-side up, push the wings upward so they make a V.

BTL-B Y-WING

CLASS: GOOD GUY

PILOT //
JON "DUTCH" VANDER

PILOT IDENTIFICATION

JOB DESCRIPTION //
GOLD LEADER IN THE BATTLE OF
YAVIN, LED Y-WINGS IN THEIR
ATTACK ON THE DEATH STAR

FAVORITE SAYING //
WE'RE STARTING OUR
ATTACK RUN!

ASTROMECH
DROID SOCKET

ION CANNON

LASER
CANNONS

DETACHABLE
COCKPIT DOUBLES
AS ESCAPE POD

PROTON TORPEDO
LAUNCHER

ABOUT MY SHIP

Y-wings are the workhorses of the Rebel fleet. These ships have been in service for a long time. Before X-wings were mass-produced, Y-wings served as the Rebellion's primary fighters. Each Y-wing has two long engine pylons. In early models, these were fully covered in armor. To make the ship more maneuverable in battles, Rebel engineers removed some of this engine plating. Y-wings have hyperdrive capability and life support for deep space travel.

WEAPONS AND DEFENSE

My ship comes equipped with two laser cannons at the front of the cockpit. It has ion cannons that shoot bursts of electricity to disable enemy ships without destroying them. This ship can be fitted with proton torpedo launchers as well. A deflector shield protects the ship during space battles.

IN BATTLE

I was a pilot in the Imperial fleet, but I defected and joined the Rebel Alliance when I was ordered to attack my home planet. I faked my ship's failure and escaped to the Rebel Alliance. As part of the Rebellion, I was promoted to leader of Gold Squadron — a fleet of Y-wing starfighters.

In the Battle of Yavin, I led one of the first Rebel attack runs against the Death Star. My fighters flew into the trench toward the exhaust port, but our aim was off, so we regrouped with the other fighters to fend off TIE fighters. We kept the Red Squadron pilots safe from harm when they zoomed through the Death Star's trench toward their final target.

BTL-B Y-WING

GREAT FOR EVERYTHING FROM BOMBING RUNS
TO SCOUTING MISSIONS, THIS REBEL SHIP
EXCELS IN CLOSE-QUARTERS COMBAT WITH
SPACE STATIONS AND LARGE STARSHIPS.
NOW YOU CAN FOLD YOUR OWN, FOR
SKIRMISHES IN THE BACKYARD AND
SCOUTING MISSIONS DOWN THE HALLWAY.

YOU WILL NEED:

Y-wing paper
Scissors
A piece of tape
A ruler

Find the paper that
looks like this. Fold it
in half lengthwise.

END UP LIKE THIS

2 Cut out the space as s
Then cut on the blue l

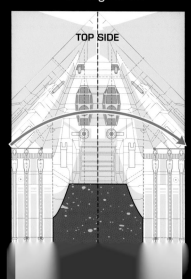

TOP SIDE

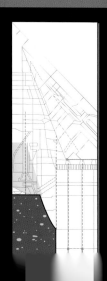

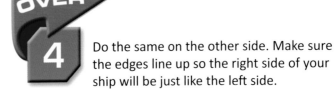

3 Pick up just the top layer of paper at the corner. Fold it down so the top edge matches up with the center fold. Crease.

4 Do the same on the other side. Make sure the edges line up so the right side of your ship will be just like the left side.

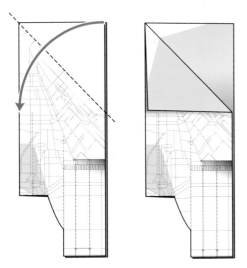

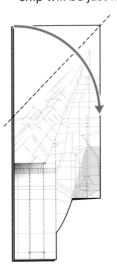

5 Unfold the fold through the middle of the paper. Lay the ship on the table with the **underside** up so it looks like the picture.

Grab one of the folded sides of the triangle and fold it to the center crease. At the top, the folded paper comes to a sharp point. At the bottom, it folds right at the end of the cut you made earlier.

Do the same on the other side.

END UP LIKE THIS

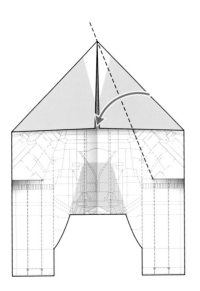

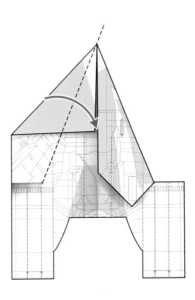

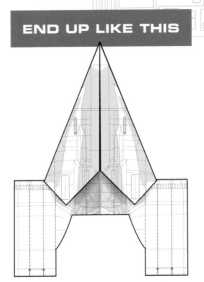

13 Fold, crease, and unfold on each of the red dashed lines on the pylon. Make sure each fold lines up exactly with one of the cuts you made for the elevator flaps.

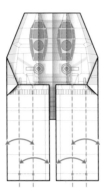

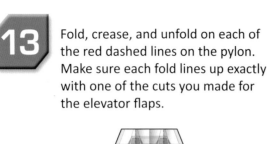

TIPS FROM A MASTER

THOSE LONG TUBES AT THE BACK OF THE Y-WING ARE CALLED PYLONS. WHEN YOU FOLD THEM, CREASE EACH FOLD WELL. THOSE CREASES MAKE THE PYLONS STIFF.

MAKE SURE YOUR STARFIGHTER LOOKS THE SAME ON BOTH SIDES. IF THE LEFT PYLON IS DIFFERENT FROM THE RIGHT, YOUR SHIP WON'T FLY STRAIGHT (IF IT FLIES AT ALL).

14 Unfold all the folds you made in steps 12 and 13. Use those folds to shape the pylons into long tubes and to give your ship a keel.

BEND THE PAPER ON THE CREASES UNTIL IT LOOKS LIKE THIS FROM THE FRONT.

KEEL

15 Your ship will look like this from the top. Push the two sides of the ship together. Put a piece of tape on top of the ship to hold the sides together.

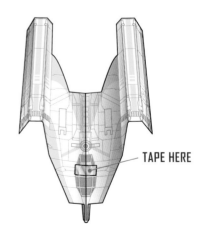

TAPE HERE

FLIP OVER

3 Pick up just the top layer of paper at the corner. Fold it down so the top edge matches up with the center fold. Crease.

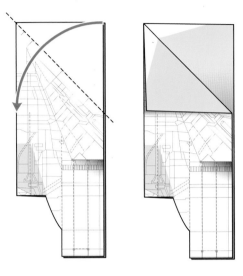

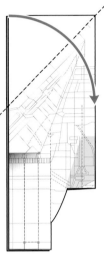

4 Do the same on the other side. Make sure the edges line up so the right side of your ship will be just like the left side.

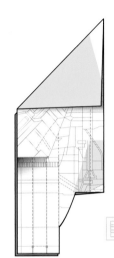

5 Unfold the fold through the middle of the paper. Lay the ship on the table with the underside up so it looks like the picture.

Grab one of the folded sides of the triangle and fold it to the center crease. At the top, the folded paper comes to a sharp point. At the bottom, it folds right at the end of the cut you made earlier.

Do the same on the other side.

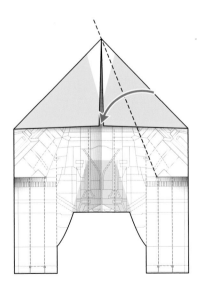

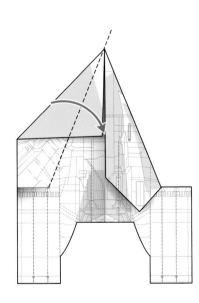

END UP LIKE THIS

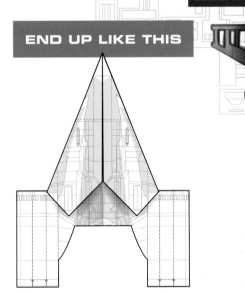

6 Fold the pointy end down like this. Flatten your fold well.

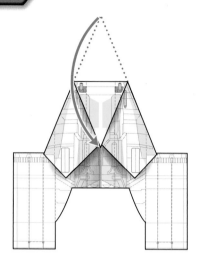

7 Fold the pointy end up so the point is right on the center crease at the top fold.

END UP LIKE THIS

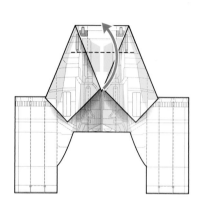

FLIP OVER

8 Refold on the center fold, with the pointy bit on the outside. There are many layers of paper at the ship's nose. Make sure that they are all creased well.

RUN YOUR FINGERNAIL OR THE EDGE OF A RULER OVER ALL YOUR FOLDS

9 Find the red dashed line that runs beside the center fold. Place the edge of your ruler on the line.

Fold the paper up, using a ruler as your guide. The edge of the ruler helps you fold straight even where there are many layers.

Once you have the fold started, put the ruler aside and complete the fold.

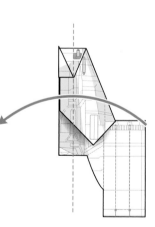

FLIP OVER

10 Fold down the other side of the ship. Match it to the one you've already folded. Crease well.

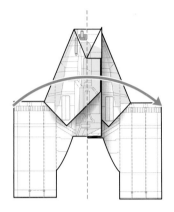 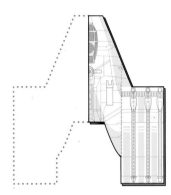

11 Flatten the ship on the table with the **top side** facing up. Your Y-wing needs elevator flaps to keep it from diving for the ground. On each side, cut on the blue lines. Then fold up on the dashed red lines, crease, and unfold to make your Y-wing's elevators.

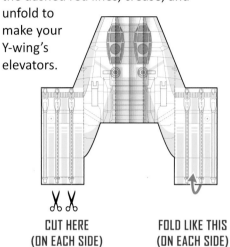

CUT HERE
(ON EACH SIDE)

FOLD LIKE THIS
(ON EACH SIDE)

12 Make sure you have the top side facing up. Now you're going to fold the pylons, the long tubes at the back of the ship. Fold on the dashed red line, as shown in the picture.

Do the same on the other side.

THIS IS THE PYLON OF YOUR Y-WING

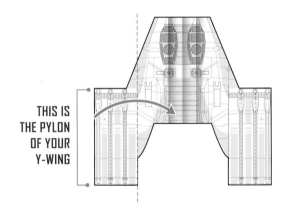 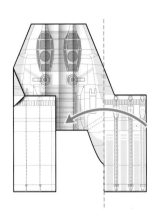

END UP LIKE THIS

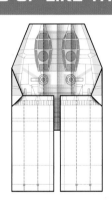

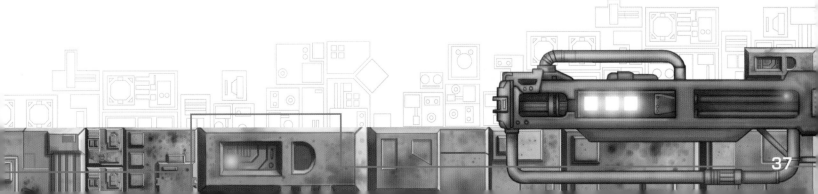

13 Fold, crease, and unfold on each of the red dashed lines on the pylon. Make sure each fold lines up exactly with one of the cuts you made for the elevator flaps.

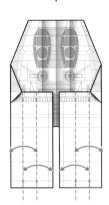

14 Unfold all the folds you made in steps 12 and 13. Use those folds to shape the pylons into long tubes and to give your ship a keel.

BEND THE PAPER ON THE CREASES UNTIL IT LOOKS LIKE THIS FROM THE FRONT.

KEEL

TIPS FROM A MASTER

THOSE LONG TUBES AT THE BACK OF THE Y-WING ARE CALLED PYLONS. WHEN YOU FOLD THEM, CREASE EACH FOLD WELL. THOSE CREASES MAKE THE PYLONS STIFF.

MAKE SURE YOUR STARFIGHTER LOOKS THE SAME ON BOTH SIDES. IF THE LEFT PYLON IS DIFFERENT FROM THE RIGHT, YOUR SHIP WON'T FLY STRAIGHT (IF IT FLIES AT ALL).

15 Your ship will look like this from the top. Push the two sides of the ship together. Put a piece of tape on top of the ship to hold the sides together.

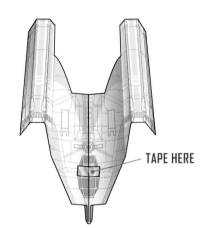

TAPE HERE

16 For your first flight, bend the elevators up just a little bit. Your ready-to-fly Y-wing looks like this.

ELEVATORS ARE
FOLDED UP JUST
A LITTLE BIT

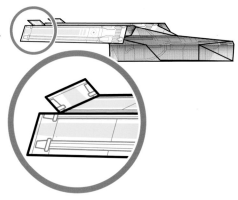

PILOT'S MANUAL //
BTL-B Y-WING

THIS SHIP IS A LONG-DISTANCE GLIDER THAT TENDS TO FLY STRAIGHT AND TRUE. HOLD THE SHIP LEVEL AND GIVE IT A MEDIUM HARD THROW.

IF YOUR SHIP DOESN'T FLY RIGHT ON YOUR FIRST TOSS:

- Check your elevators. If your ship climbed steeply, flatten them a little. If your ship dove for the ground, push the elevators up a little.

- Straighten out any stray bends or curves in the paper.

- Make sure the pylons are straight and parallel to each other.

- If your ship rolls to the left, lower the right elevator. If it rolls right, lower the left elevator.

- Don't throw the ship quite so hard.

TIE ADVANCED X1

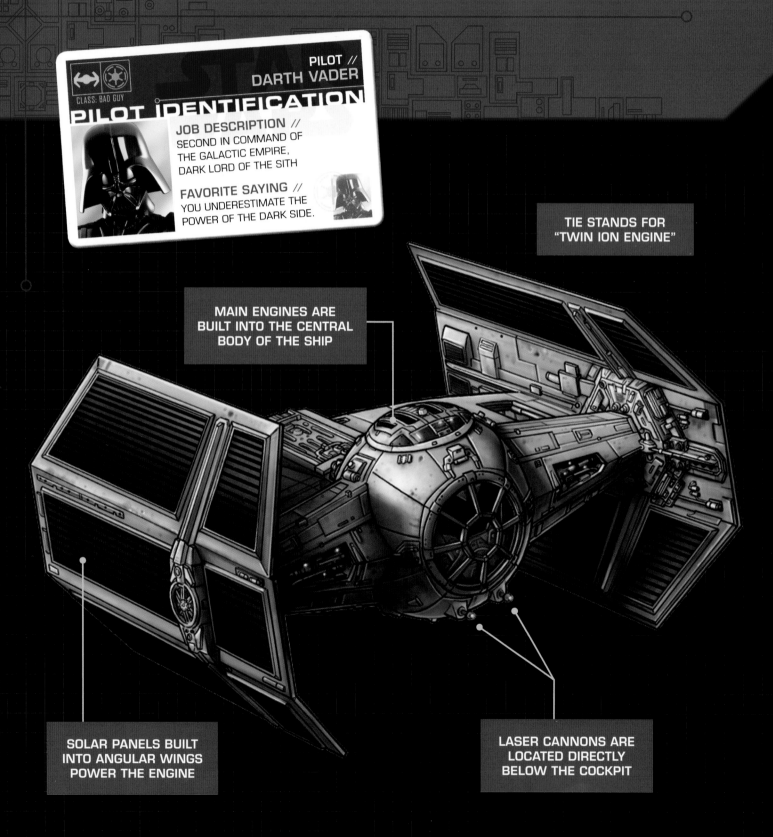

PILOT //
DARTH VADER

CLASS: BAD GUY

PILOT IDENTIFICATION

JOB DESCRIPTION //
SECOND IN COMMAND OF
THE GALACTIC EMPIRE,
DARK LORD OF THE SITH

FAVORITE SAYING //
YOU UNDERESTIMATE THE
POWER OF THE DARK SIDE.

TIE STANDS FOR
"TWIN ION ENGINE"

MAIN ENGINES ARE
BUILT INTO THE CENTRAL
BODY OF THE SHIP

SOLAR PANELS BUILT
INTO ANGULAR WINGS
POWER THE ENGINE

LASER CANNONS ARE
LOCATED DIRECTLY
BELOW THE COCKPIT

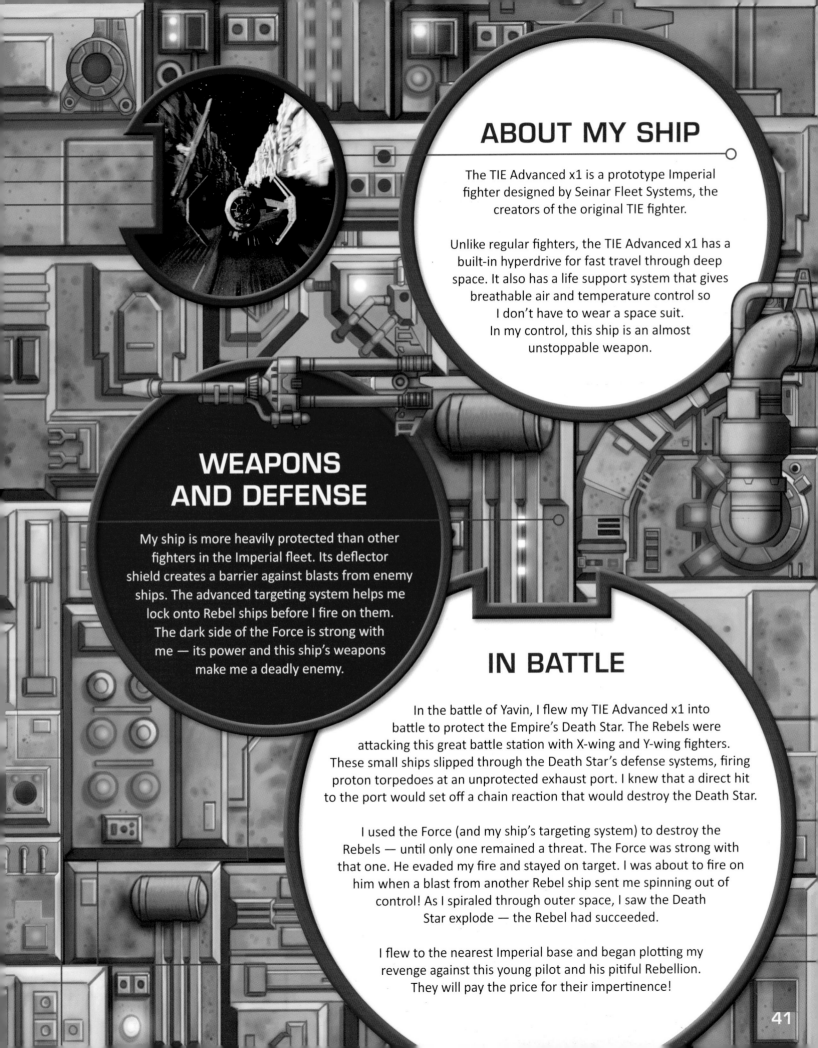

ABOUT MY SHIP

The TIE Advanced x1 is a prototype Imperial fighter designed by Seinar Fleet Systems, the creators of the original TIE fighter.

Unlike regular fighters, the TIE Advanced x1 has a built-in hyperdrive for fast travel through deep space. It also has a life support system that gives breathable air and temperature control so I don't have to wear a space suit. In my control, this ship is an almost unstoppable weapon.

WEAPONS AND DEFENSE

My ship is more heavily protected than other fighters in the Imperial fleet. Its deflector shield creates a barrier against blasts from enemy ships. The advanced targeting system helps me lock onto Rebel ships before I fire on them. The dark side of the Force is strong with me — its power and this ship's weapons make me a deadly enemy.

IN BATTLE

In the battle of Yavin, I flew my TIE Advanced x1 into battle to protect the Empire's Death Star. The Rebels were attacking this great battle station with X-wing and Y-wing fighters. These small ships slipped through the Death Star's defense systems, firing proton torpedoes at an unprotected exhaust port. I knew that a direct hit to the port would set off a chain reaction that would destroy the Death Star.

I used the Force (and my ship's targeting system) to destroy the Rebels — until only one remained a threat. The Force was strong with that one. He evaded my fire and stayed on target. I was about to fire on him when a blast from another Rebel ship sent me spinning out of control! As I spiraled through outer space, I saw the Death Star explode — the Rebel had succeeded.

I flew to the nearest Imperial base and began plotting my revenge against this young pilot and his pitiful Rebellion. They will pay the price for their impertinence!

TIE ADVANCED X1

THE TIE ADVANCED X1 IS A FIRST FOR THE IMPERIAL NAVY: A STARFIGHTER WITH SHIELDS AND HYPERDRIVE. RESERVED FOR SPECIAL SQUADRONS, THIS ELITE FIGHTER WAS FAR TOO EXPENSIVE TO MASS-PRODUCE… UNTIL NOW. WITH SOME CAREFUL CUTTING-EDGE FOLDING (AND CUTTING), YOU CAN MAKE A SQUADRON OF FIVE PAPER FIGHTERS, A FORCE UNEQUALLED IN THE GALAXY.

YOU WILL NEED:

- TIE fighter wing paper
- TIE fighter hull paper
- Scissors
- 9 pieces of tape
- A ruler

MAKE IT — THE WING

1 Find the paper that looks like this. Cut off the strip at the end as shown.

END UP LIKE THIS

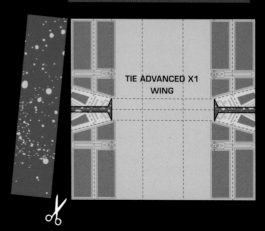

TIE ADVANCED X1
WING

2 Turn the paper so the words are right-side-up. Fold in half lengthwise, like this.

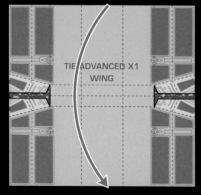

TIE ADVANCED X1
WING

3 Cut on the solid blue lines. Throw away the extra bits.

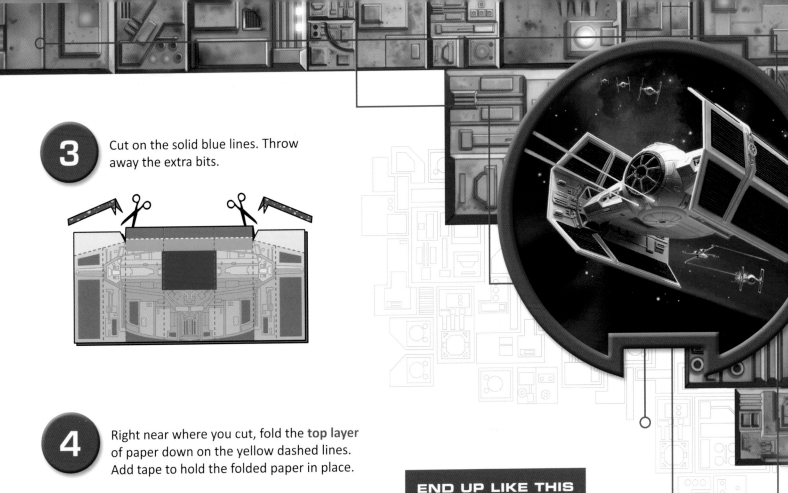

4 Right near where you cut, fold the **top layer** of paper down on the yellow dashed lines. Add tape to hold the folded paper in place.

FOLD TOP LAYER ONLY

END UP LIKE THIS

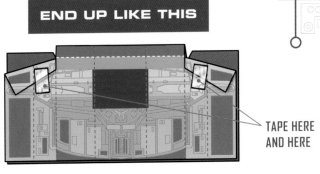

TAPE HERE
AND HERE

5 Fold the top layer in on the two green dashed lines. Crease and unfold.

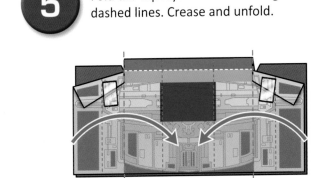

6 Fold the top layer in on the two blue dashed lines. Crease and unfold.

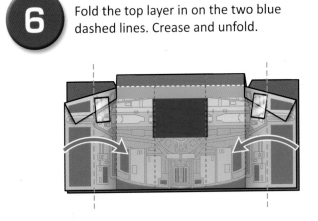

FLIP OVER

7

After you flip the wing over, it will look like this. Repeat steps 4–6 on this side.

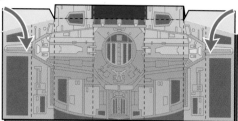

END UP LIKE THIS

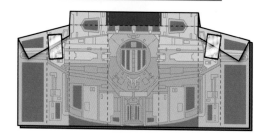

FLIP OVER

8

Fold the red rectangle down so it covers the orange rectangle.

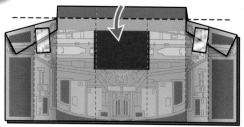

END UP LIKE THIS

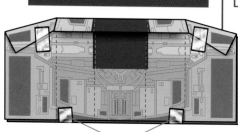

TAPE HERE AND HERE

TAPE THE TOP AND BOTTOM LAYERS TOGETHER AT THE BOTTOM EDGE OF THE WING.

FLIP OVER

9

Find these two purple dashed lines. Fold on each one, crease, and unfold. This time, fold both layers.

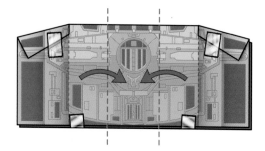

10

Grab the wing at the folded edge, with one hand near each of the folds you just made. Pull the center section — the part between your latest folds — across a table edge to make it curl a little.

GRAB HERE AND HERE

CURL THIS SECTION ONLY

MAKE SURE THE FOLDED LAYER IS AGAINST THE TABLE

SET THE WING ASIDE. TIME TO FOLD THE HULL.

TIE ADVANCED X1
MAKE IT — THE HULL

THE TIE ADVANCED X1 HAS A SUPER-STRONG HULL, BUILT WITH DURASTEEL TO WITHSTAND ENEMY FIRE. THE HULL YOU'RE FOLDING IS NOT DURASTEEL. BUT YOU'LL FOLD MANY LAYERS, SO IT'S MIGHTY STRONG... FOR PAPER.

1 Start with paper that looks like this. Cut on the solid blue line. You'll fold one of the two pieces — and save the other for another TIE fighter.

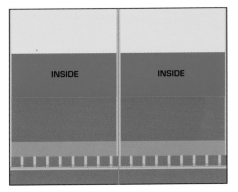

2 Start with the **inside** facing up. Fold the paper in half, top to bottom. Crease and unfold.

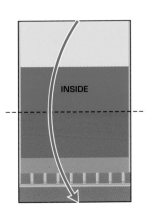

3 Fold the bright yellow rectangle on top of the turquoise rectangle. Crease well.

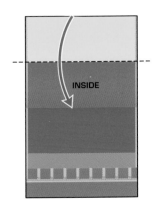

4 Fold the lime green rectangle on top of the red rectangle. Crease well.

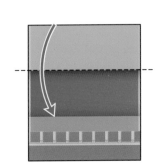

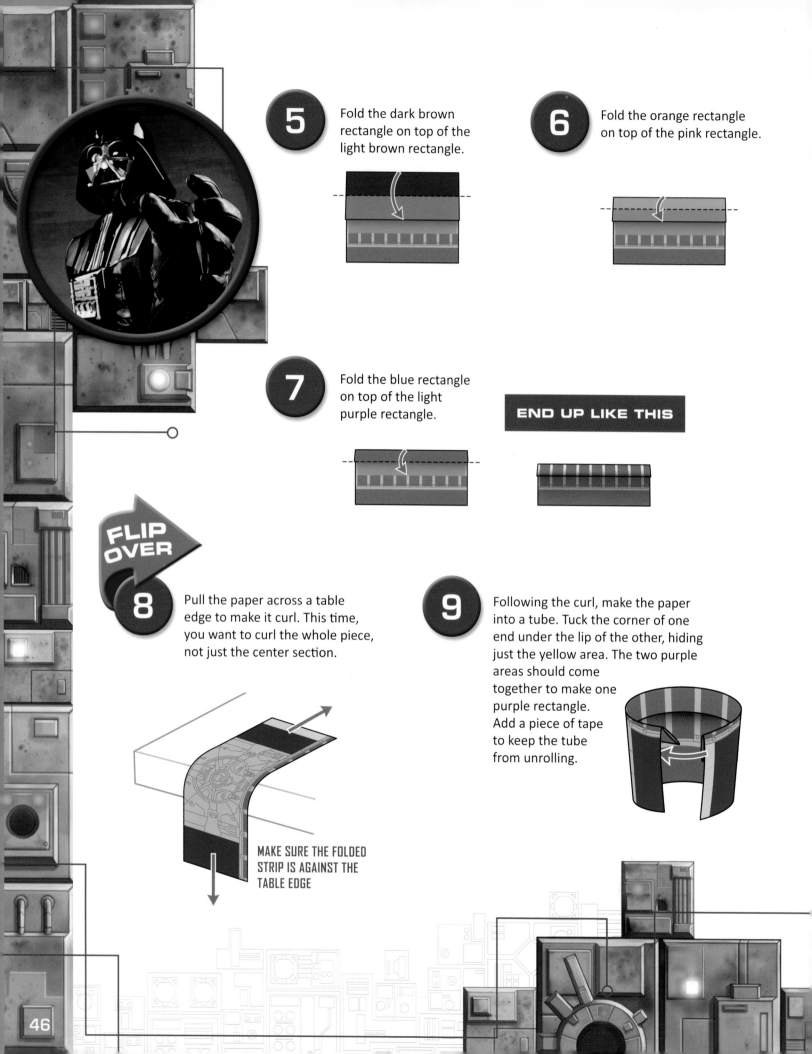

5 Fold the dark brown rectangle on top of the light brown rectangle.

6 Fold the orange rectangle on top of the pink rectangle.

7 Fold the blue rectangle on top of the light purple rectangle.

END UP LIKE THIS

FLIP OVER

8 Pull the paper across a table edge to make it curl. This time, you want to curl the whole piece, not just the center section.

MAKE SURE THE FOLDED STRIP IS AGAINST THE TABLE EDGE

9 Following the curl, make the paper into a tube. Tuck the corner of one end under the lip of the other, hiding just the yellow area. The two purple areas should come together to make one purple rectangle. Add a piece of tape to keep the tube from unrolling.

TIE ADVANCED X1
PUT IT TOGETHER

1 Find the purple areas on the wing and the hull. Place the hull on the wing so both purple areas are hidden.

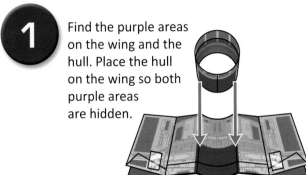

2 Fold the wing down on the purple dashed line. Pinch the hull and wing together. Position the hull so you can see the edge of the purple area on the hull. Tape the hull in place.

TAPE HERE

LINE UP THE FRONT EDGE OF THE HULL WITH THE FRONT EDGE OF THE WING

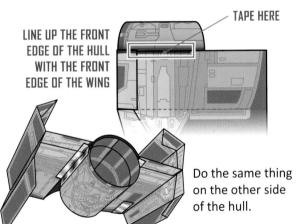

Do the same thing on the other side of the hull.

3 Fold the solar panels so they look like this.

PILOT'S MANUAL //
TIE ADVANCED X1

THIS SHIP FLIES LIKE NO OTHER PAPER FLYER WE'VE EVER SEEN. IT'S JUST AS HAPPY FLYING ON ITS SIDE — OR UPSIDE DOWN. IT LOOPS AND — MORE OFTEN THAN NOT — SWOOPS BACK TO ATTACK THE PERSON WHO THREW IT.

WE SUGGEST TWO DIFFERENT LAUNCHING METHODS.

HOLD THE HULL AND TOSS THE SHIP FORWARD AND UP.

OR

GRAB THE BACK OF THE WING AND TOSS THE SHIP STRAIGHT UP.

THE KEY IS TO SEND THE SHIP UPWARD, SO IT HAS ROOM TO SWOOP WITHOUT HITTING THE FLOOR.

IF YOUR SHIP DOESN'T FLY RIGHT ON YOUR FIRST TOSS:

- Make sure the front edge of the wing and the front edge of the hull are lined up.

- Make your wings look like the ones in the picture.

- Check that the top and bottom layers of the wing are taped together.

T-65 X-WING

THRUST ENGINES

COCKPIT

LASER CANNONS

LASER CANNONS

ONBOARD
ASTROMECH DROID

ABOUT MY SHIP

The T-65 X-wing gets its name from its special wings. In normal flight, the wings lock together. In battle, they split apart and become four wings in the shape of an X.

When first built, the X-wing was the most advanced starfighter in the galaxy. The ship is equipped with life support and a hyperdrive. It can carry a pilot and one astromech droid — I fly with R2-D2.

WEAPONS AND DEFENSE

My X-wing has a laser cannon on the tip of each wing and a proton torpedo launcher. A deflector shield projector protects my ship from damaging enemy blasts.

IN BATTLE

In the Battle of Yavin, our mission was to attack the Death Star. We knew that firing a proton torpedo into the space station's exhaust system would set off a reaction that would blow it up. I had plenty of practice racing a T-16 skyhopper through Beggar's Canyon on my home planet, Tatooine, so flying an X-wing was no problem for me.

As we flew toward the Death Star, TIE fighters attacked us. With the help of my friend Biggs, I dodged all of them. By the time I made my attack run along the Death Star trench, I was one of the few remaining Rebel pilots. I had three TIE fighters on my tail, but in the nick of time my friend Han Solo blasted one of them. Using the Force, I fired two torpedoes at the port and they went in. The remaining Rebels flew back to base as the Death Star exploded.

T-65 X-WING

THE WINGS OF THE X-WING FIGHTER FORM AN X WHEN THE SHIP IS IN ATTACK POSITION. THIS GIVES THE WING-TIP LASERS A LARGER FIRING AREA. THE. YOUR PAPER X-WING IS ALWAYS READY TO ATTACK.

THIS IS THE TRICKIEST STARFIGHTER TO FOLD — BUT IT'S WORTH THE EFFORT.

YOU WILL NEED:

- X-wing wing paper (left and right)
- X-wing hull paper
- Scissors
- 13 pieces of tape
- A ruler

MAKE IT — THE WINGS

1 There are three wings on each sheet of X-wing wing paper. Cut out one right wing and one left wing. Save the other wings for another ship.

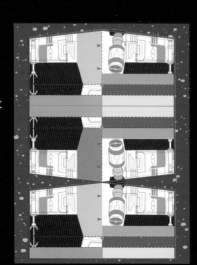

END UP LIKE THIS

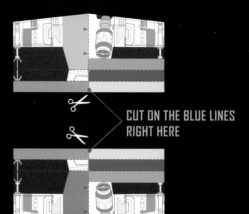

CUT ON THE BLUE LINES RIGHT HERE

2

Lay the right wing down as shown. Fold the yellow rectangle on top of the red rectangle, exposing an orange rectangle.

END UP LIKE THIS

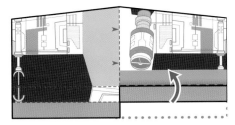

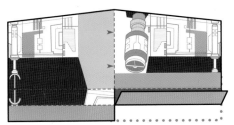

3

Fold that orange rectangle on top of the green rectangle. Crease well and add tape.

END UP LIKE THIS

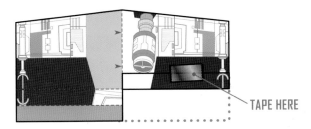

TAPE HERE

FLIP OVER

4

Flip the wing over. Repeat steps 2 and 3 on this side.

END UP LIKE THIS

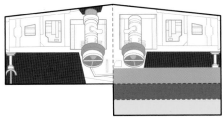

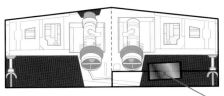

TAPE HERE

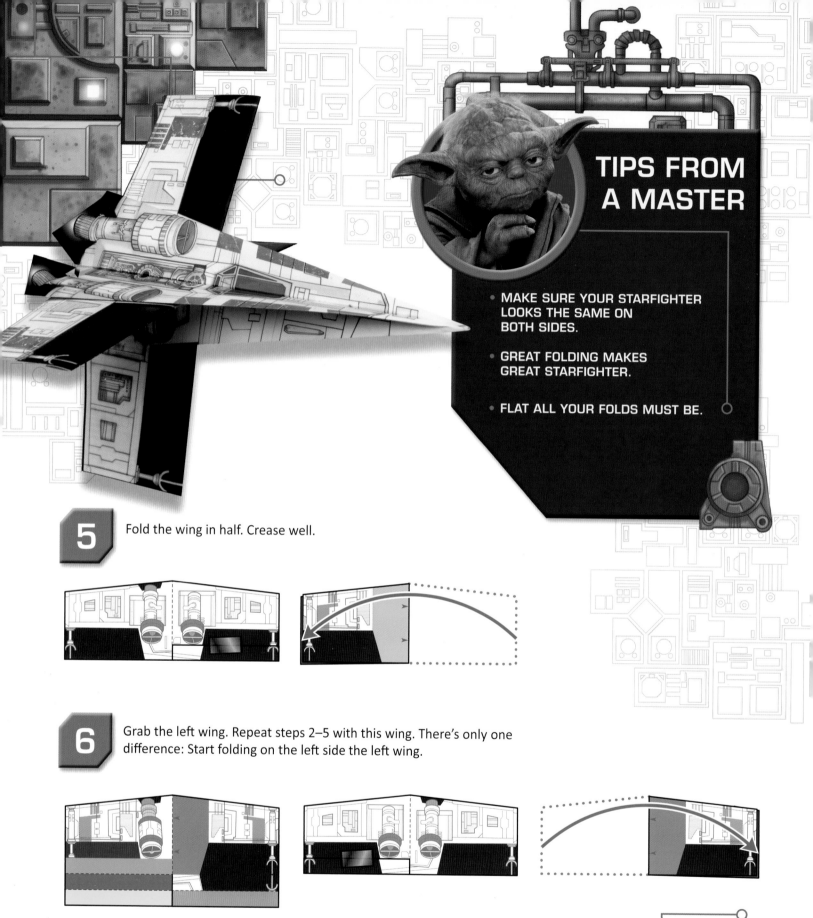

TIPS FROM A MASTER

- MAKE SURE YOUR STARFIGHTER LOOKS THE SAME ON BOTH SIDES.

- GREAT FOLDING MAKES GREAT STARFIGHTER.

- FLAT ALL YOUR FOLDS MUST BE.

5 Fold the wing in half. Crease well.

6 Grab the left wing. Repeat steps 2–5 with this wing. There's only one difference: Start folding on the left side the left wing.

SET THE WINGS ASIDE.
TIME TO FOLD THE HULL.

T-65 X-WING
MAKE IT — THE HULL

CREATED FOR THE REBEL ALLIANCE BY THE INCOM CORPORATION, THE X-WING WAS KEPT SECRET FROM THE EMPIRE. FORTUNATELY FOR YOU, KLUTZ LABS WAS ABLE TO OBTAIN COPIES OF THE TOP-SECRET PLANS.

1 Find the paper that looks like this. Cut off the space at one end and throw it away.

END UP LIKE THIS

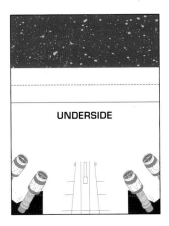

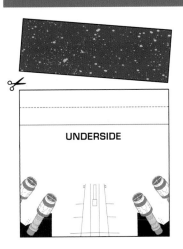

2 Make sure the **underside** is facing up. Fold the top edge down so it lands right at the green line. A dashed red line shows where to fold. Crease well.

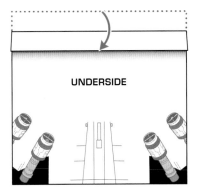

FLIP OVER

3 Fold in half like this. Crease well and unfold.

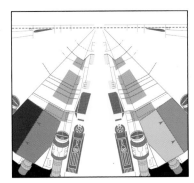

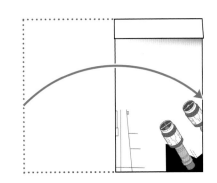

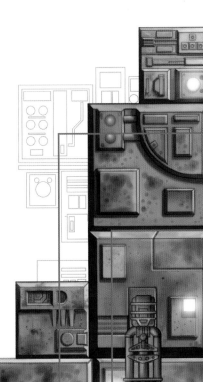

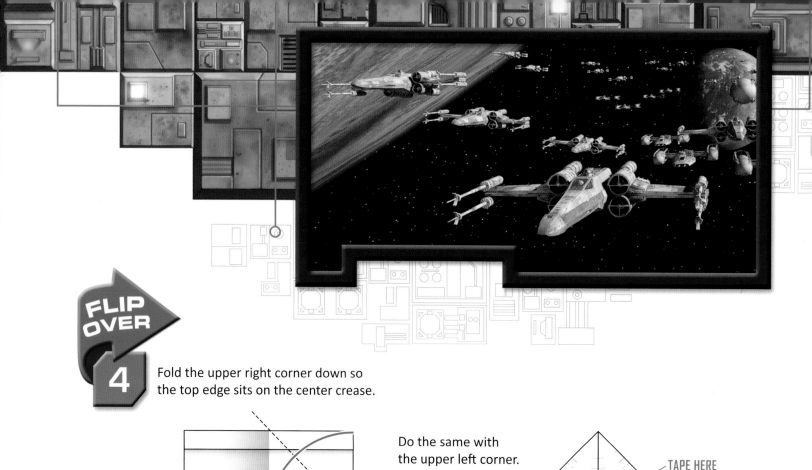

FLIP OVER

4 Fold the upper right corner down so the top edge sits on the center crease.

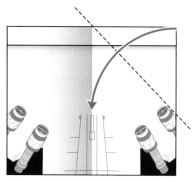

Do the same with the upper left corner. Crease well and add tape where the corners meet.

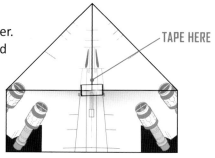

TAPE HERE

5 Fold the upper right edge so it sits right on the center crease.

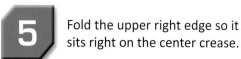

END UP LIKE THIS

Do the same with the upper left edge. Flatten all your folds.

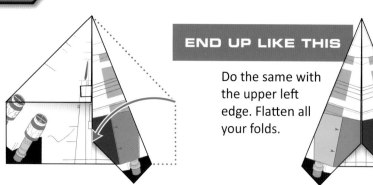

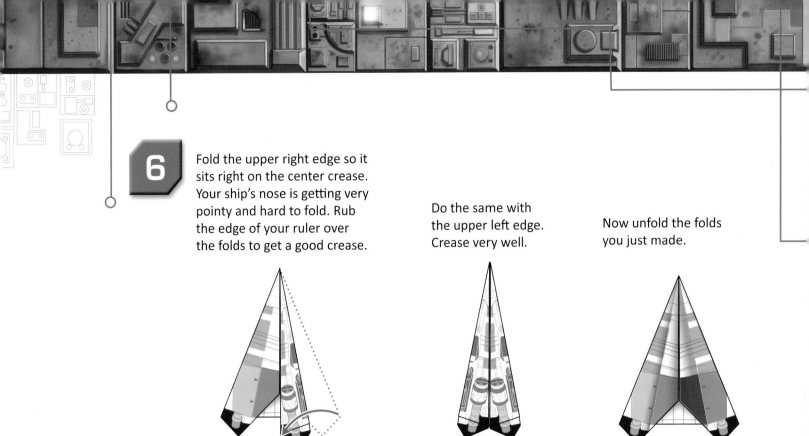

6 Fold the upper right edge so it sits right on the center crease. Your ship's nose is getting very pointy and hard to fold. Rub the edge of your ruler over the folds to get a good crease.

Do the same with the upper left edge. Crease very well.

Now unfold the folds you just made.

FLIP OVER

7 Push the sides together. Put a piece of tape on the cockpit to hold them in place.

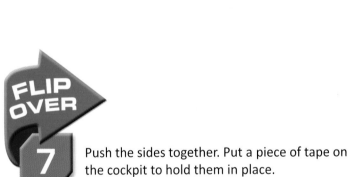

TAPE HERE

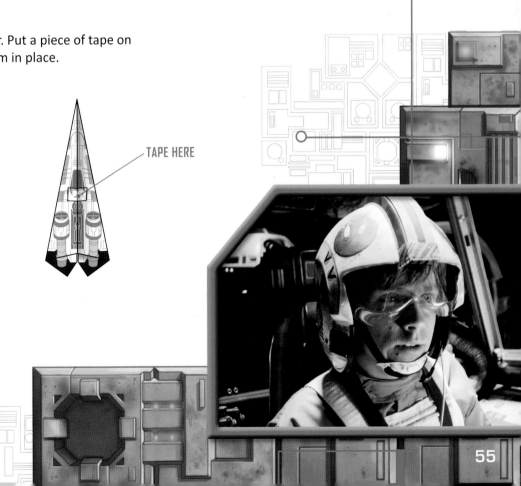

T-65 X-WING
PUT IT TOGETHER

YOUR FINAL TASK IS ATTACHING THE WINGS TO THE HULL. IT'S A LITTLE TRICKY, BUT SAVING THE GALAXY ISN'T EASY. WE KNOW YOU CAN DO IT.

1 Flatten your hull along existing creases so you can see the words "Right Wing." Hold your folded right wing so you can see the words "Right Wing."

2 Put the wing on the hull so it covers the words. Move the wing so the arrows on the wing point right at the arrows on the hull. Make sure the fold in the wing is right on the fold in the hull. Tape the wing to the hull.

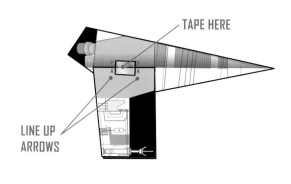

TAPE HERE

LINE UP ARROWS

3 Fold up the wing and the top layer of the hull.

YOUR SHIP WILL LOOK LIKE THIS.

4 Tape in two places as shown.

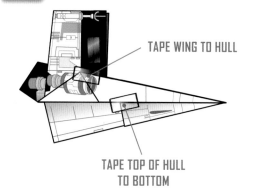

TAPE WING TO HULL

TAPE TOP OF HULL TO BOTTOM

5 Flip the ship over and flatten it on existing creases so you can see the words "Left Wing." Find your left wing and repeat steps 1–4 on this side.

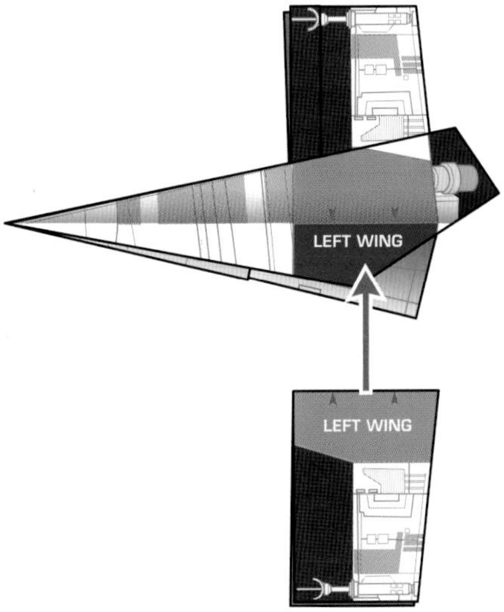

LEFT WING

LEFT WING

END UP LIKE THIS

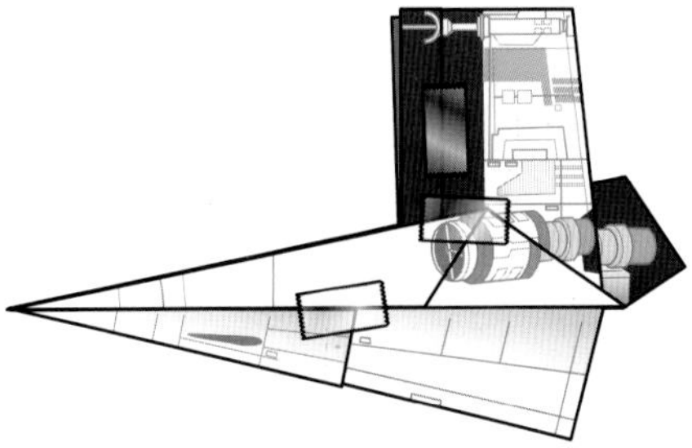

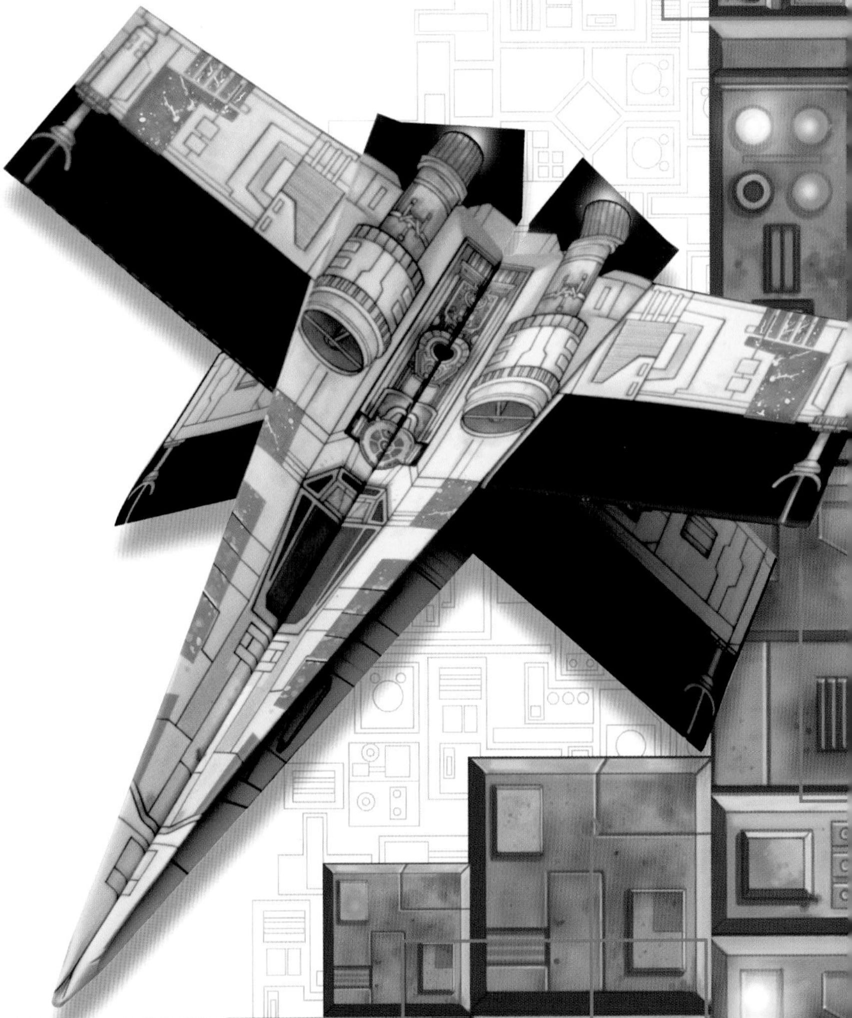

6 Find the top of the ship. Flatten the ship along existing creases so it looks like this. Tape both wings in place.

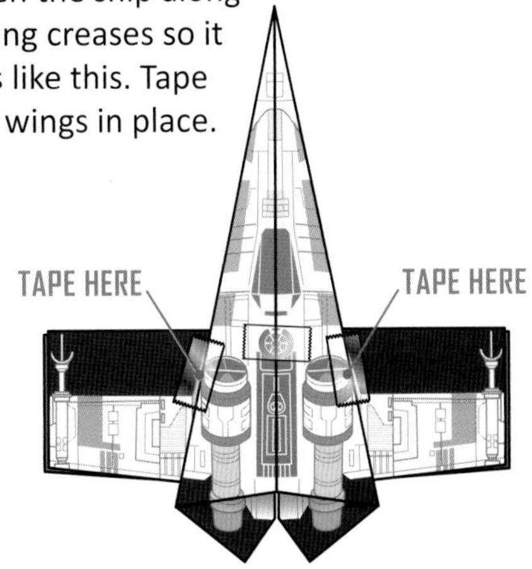

TAPE HERE   TAPE HERE

7 At the back of the ship are elevators. When you fold them just right, they make the nose of the ship rise. Fold on the dashed line, crease, and unfold.

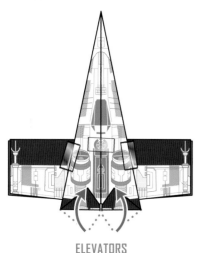

ELEVATORS

8 Point the ship's nose (the pointy end) away from you.

OPEN UP THE FOLDS SO THE HULL LOOKS LIKE THIS FROM THE BACK.

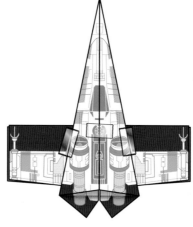

YOU'RE READY TO FLY

PILOT'S MANUAL //
T-65 X-WING

THIS SHIP IS THE TRICKIEST TO FOLD AND THE TRICKIEST TO FLY. IT FLIES LIKE A DART — MOVING FAST FOR SHORT DISTANCES. HOLD THE SHIP BY THE KEEL AT THE BOTTOM. SET YOUR ELEVATORS AT A 45-DEGREE ANGLE. HOLD THE SHIP LEVEL AND GIVE IT A MEDIUM HARD THROW, KEEPING IT LEVEL AS YOU LET GO.

SIDE VIEW

ELEVATOR

45°

SHIP HULL

IF YOUR SHIP DOESN'T FLY RIGHT ON YOUR FIRST TOSS:

• Check your elevators. If your ship climbed steeply, flatten them a little. If your ship dove for the ground, push the elevators up a little.

• Flatten out the top of the ship.

• Don't throw the ship quite so hard.

• Be sure to keep the ship level when you release it.

DISPLAY YOUR SHIPS WITH PRIDE

WE HAVE INCLUDED AN EASY-TO-BUILD DISPLAY STAND FOR EACH SHIP.

1 Carefully cut out the stand you want to make.

2 Fold it in half lengthwise and cut out the shapes on the fold.

3 Fold and unfold on each dashed ine.

4 Insert one end of the paper strip into the other end. Tape.

TAPE HERE

SHIPBUILDING MATERIALS

IN THE FOLLOWING PAGES, YOU'LL FIND
THE TAPE AND PAPER PARTS YOU NEED
(WITH A FEW SPARES) TO CREATE
A FLEET OF 30 STARFIGHTERS.

HERE'S WHAT YOU GET:

NABOO N-1 STARFIGHTER //
5 SHEETS OF PAPER TO MAKE 5 SHIPS

JEDI STARFIGHTER //
5 SHEETS OF PAPER
TO MAKE 5 SHIPS

MILLENNIUM FALCON //
5 SHEETS OF PAPER
TO MAKE 5 SHIPS

Y-WING //
5 SHEETS OF PAPER
TO MAKE 5 SHIPS

TIE ADVANCED X1 //
5 SHEETS OF PAPER TO
MAKE 5 WINGS

3 SHEETS OF PAPER TO
MAKE 6 HULLS
(YOU GET ONE SPARE HULL)

X-WING //
5 SHEETS OF PAPER TO
MAKE 5 HULLS

4 SHEETS OF PAPER TO MAKE
6 SETS OF WINGS
(YOU GET ONE SPARE SET OF WINGS)

DISPLAY STANDS //
3 SHEETS OF PAPER TO MAKE
6 DISPLAY STANDS (ONE FOR EACH
MODEL OF STARFIGHTER)

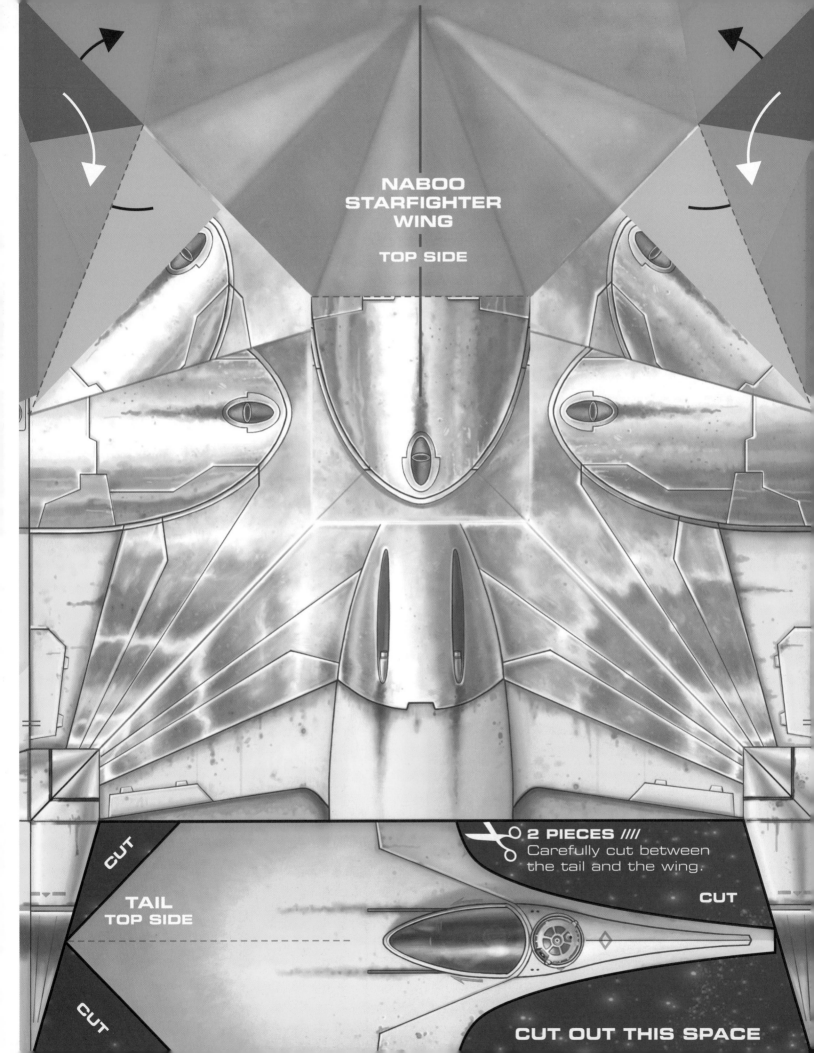

NABOO
STARFIGHTER
WING

TOP SIDE

CUT

TAIL
TOP SIDE

✂ 2 PIECES ////
Carefully cut between
the tail and the wing.

CUT

CUT

CUT OUT THIS SPACE

NABOO
STARFIGHTER
WING

UNDERSIDE

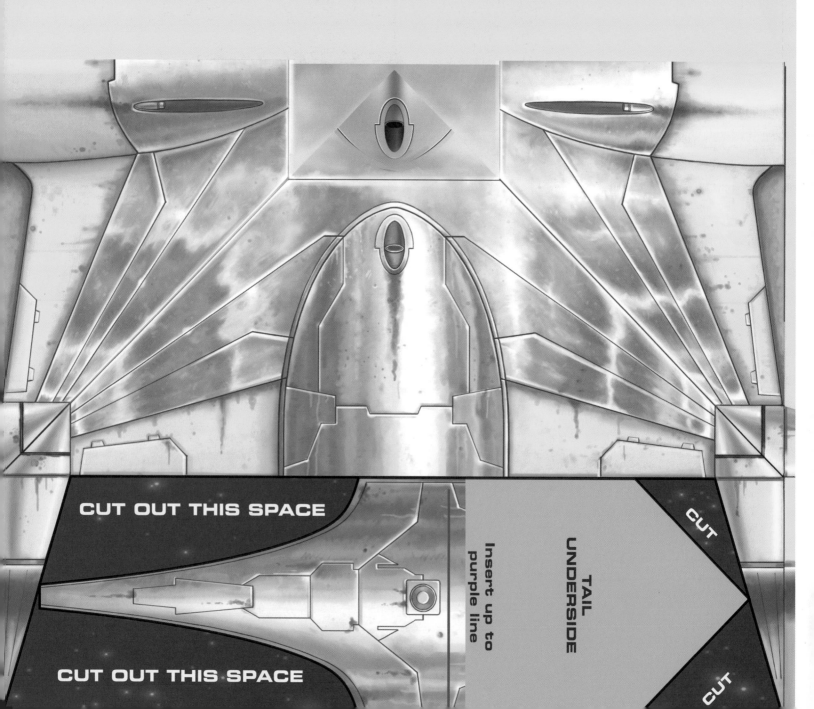

CUT OUT THIS SPACE

CUT OUT THIS SPACE

Insert up to
purple line

TAIL
UNDERSIDE

CUT

CUT

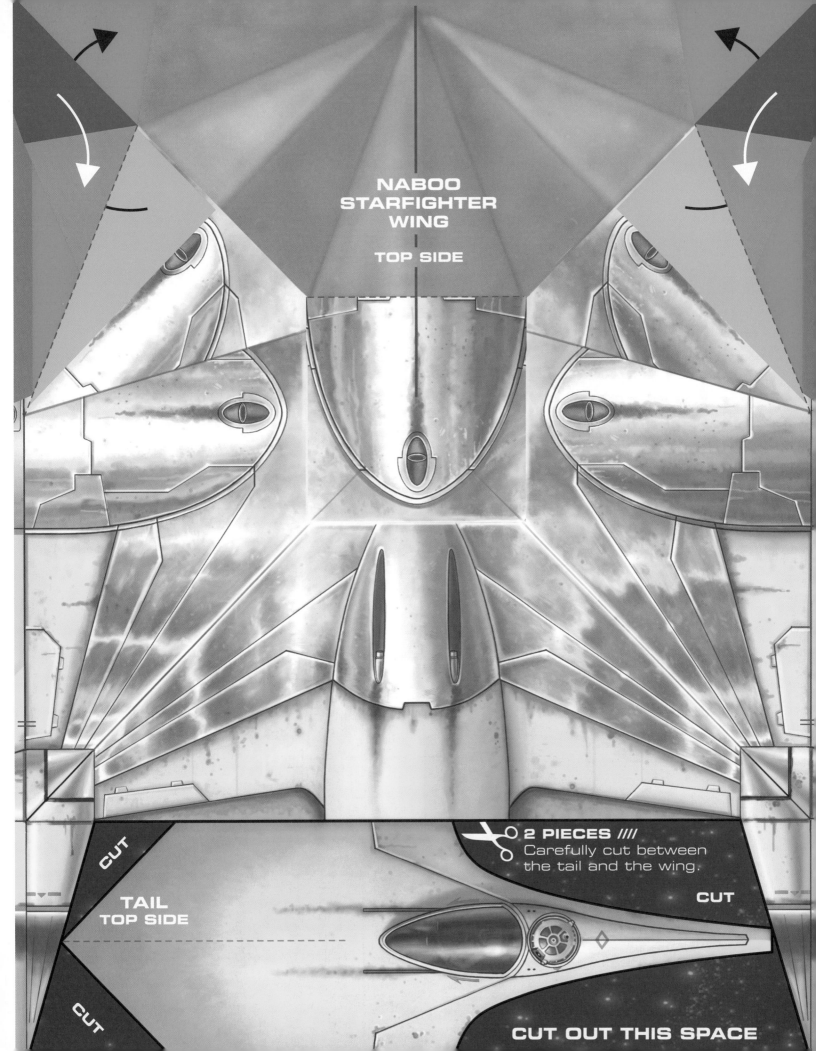

NABOO STARFIGHTER WING

TOP SIDE

CUT

TAIL
TOP SIDE

CUT

CUT

2 PIECES ////
Carefully cut between
the tail and the wing.

CUT

CUT OUT THIS SPACE

NABOO
STARFIGHTER
WING

UNDERSIDE

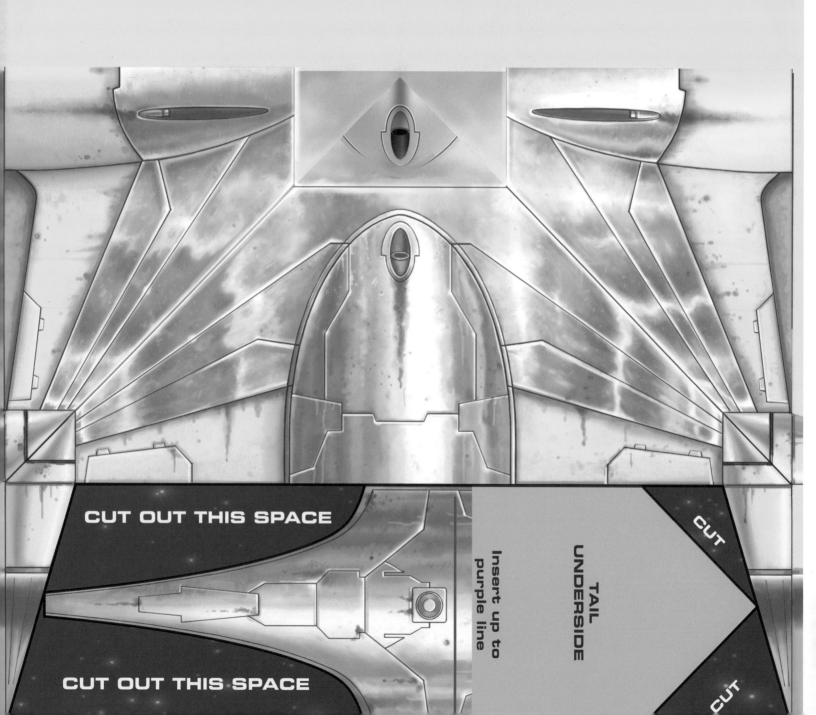

CUT OUT THIS SPACE

CUT OUT THIS SPACE

Insert up to
purple line

TAIL
UNDERSIDE

CUT

CUT

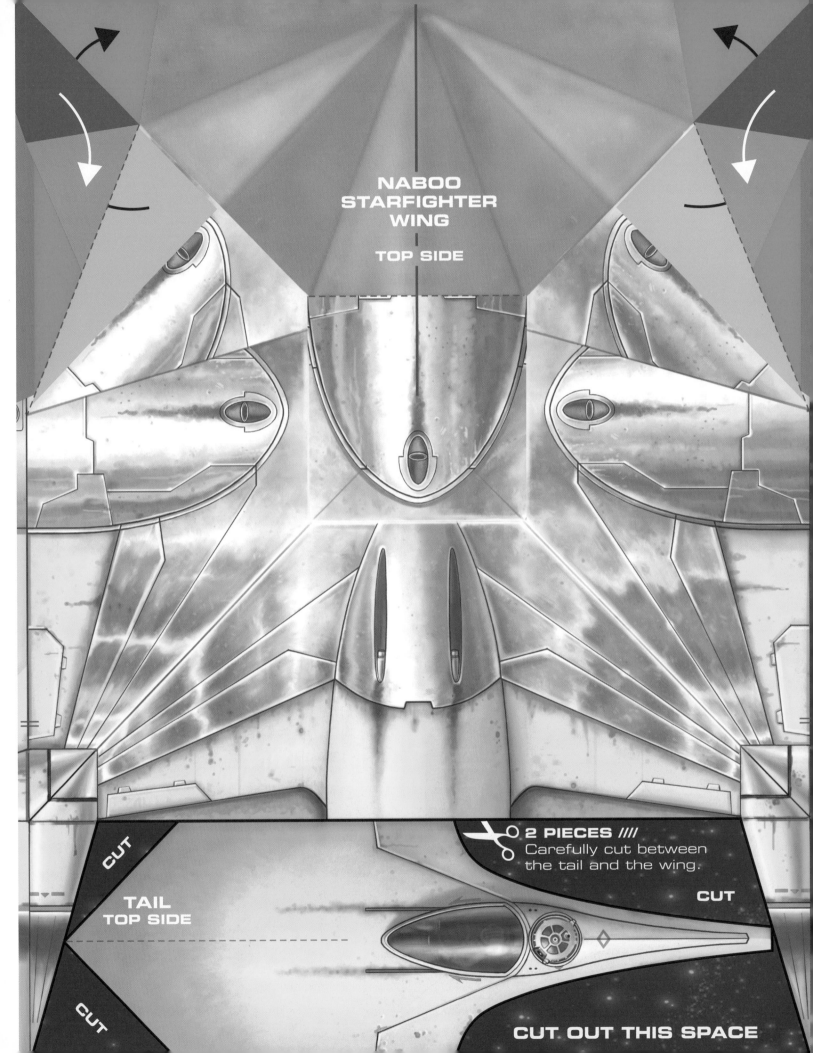

NABOO
STARFIGHTER
WING

TOP SIDE

CUT

TAIL
TOP SIDE

2 PIECES ////
Carefully cut between
the tail and the wing.

CUT

CUT

CUT OUT THIS SPACE

NABOO
STARFIGHTER
WING

UNDERSIDE

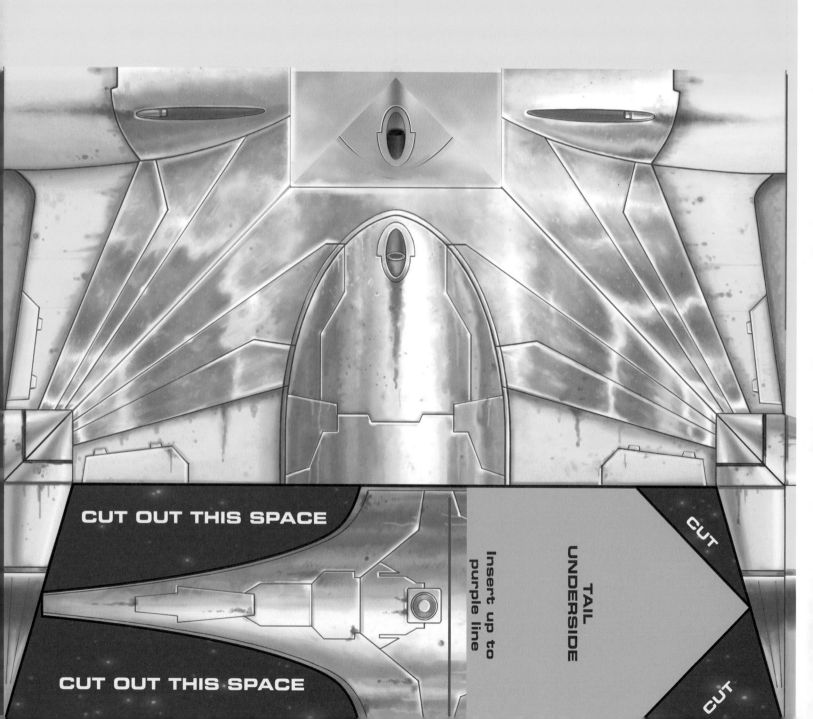

CUT OUT THIS SPACE

CUT OUT THIS SPACE

Insert up to purple line

TAIL UNDERSIDE

CUT

CUT

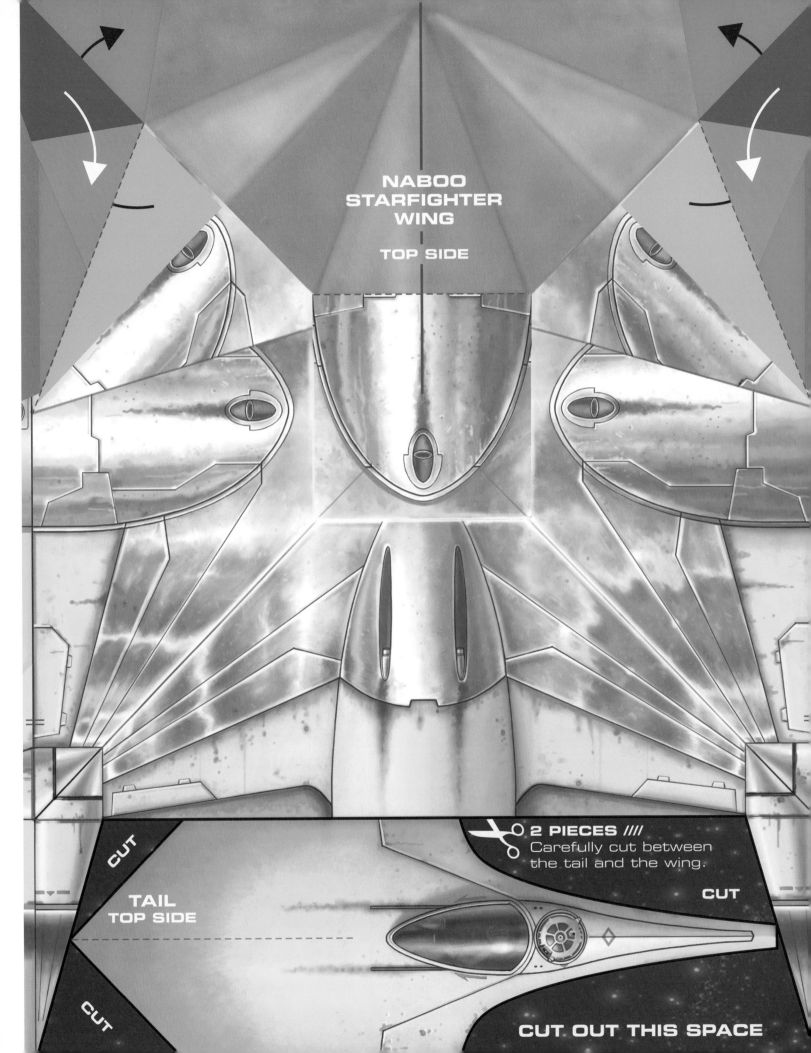

NABOO
STARFIGHTER
WING

TOP SIDE

CUT

TAIL
TOP SIDE

✂ 2 PIECES ////
Carefully cut between
the tail and the wing.

CUT

CUT

CUT OUT THIS SPACE

NABOO
STARFIGHTER
WING

UNDERSIDE

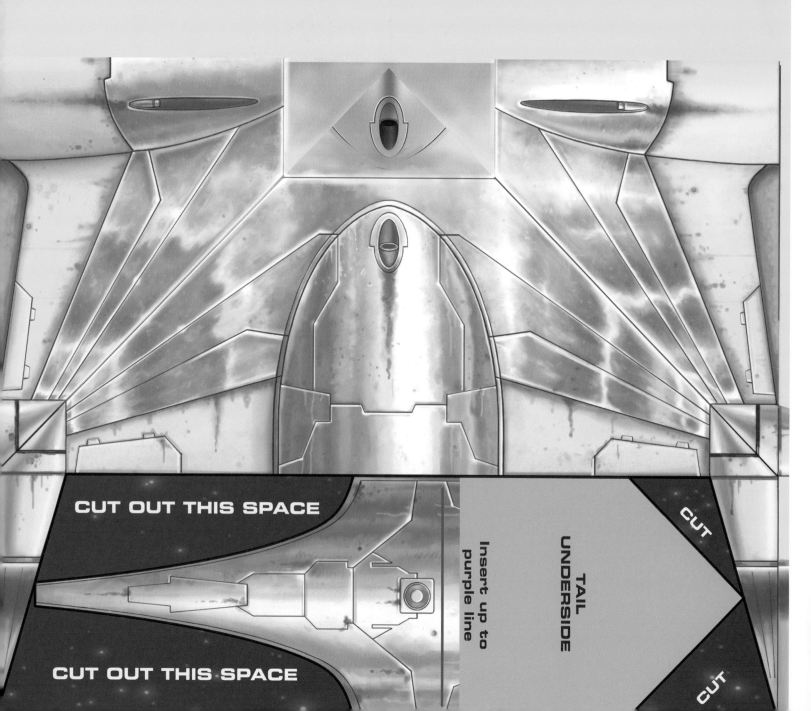

CUT OUT THIS SPACE

CUT OUT THIS SPACE

Insert up to
purple line

TAIL
UNDERSIDE

CUT

CUT

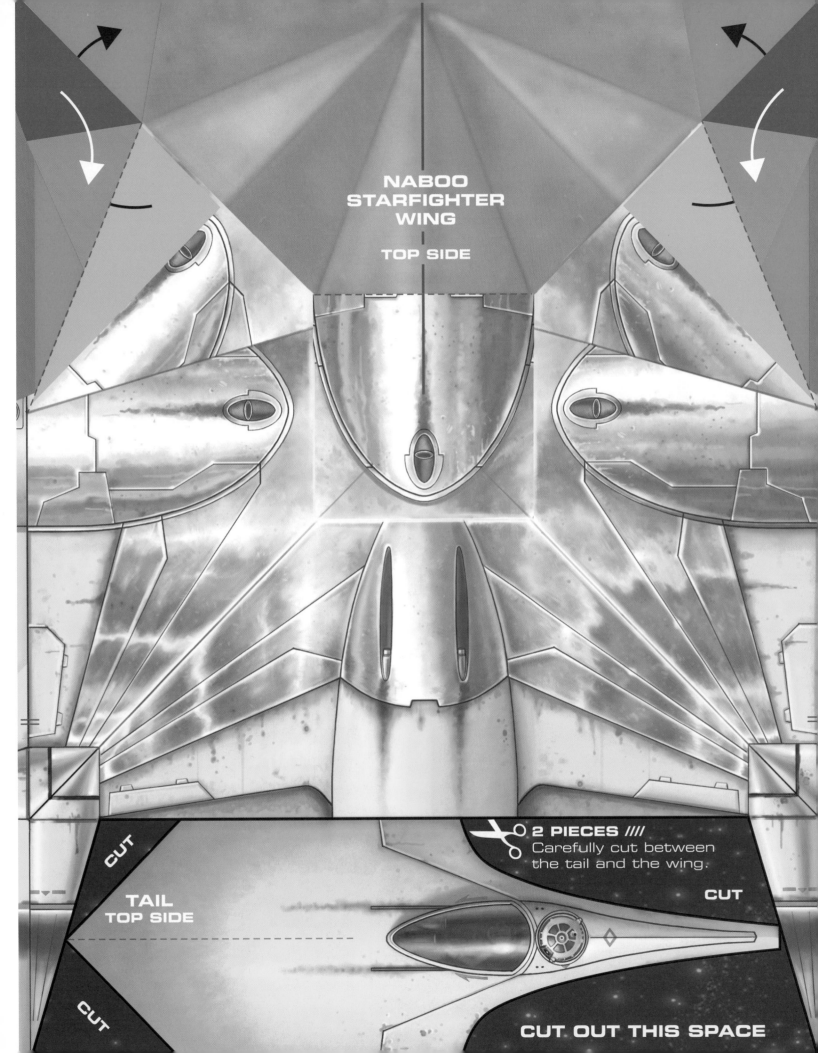

NABOO
STARFIGHTER
WING

UNDERSIDE

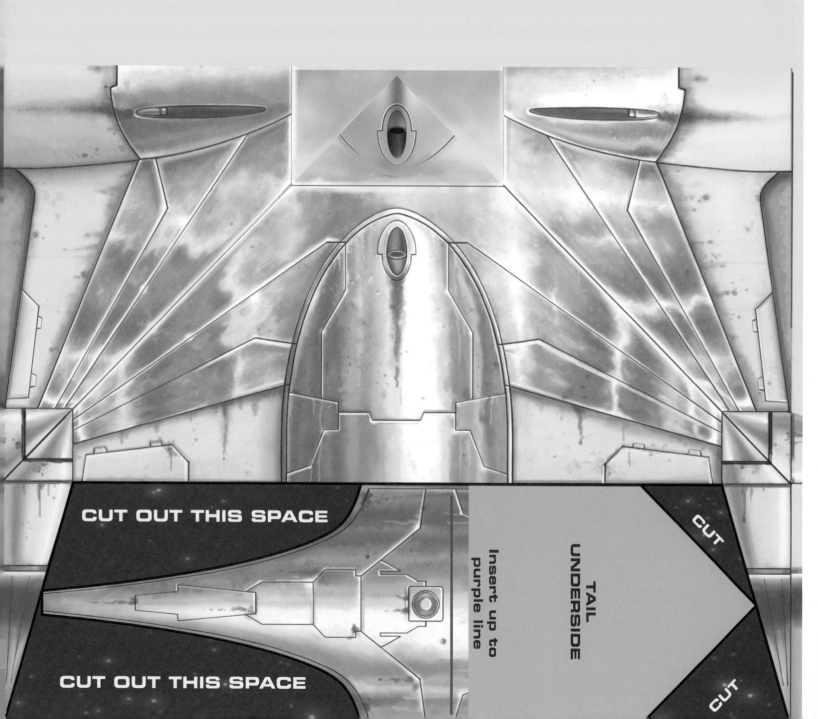

CUT OUT THIS SPACE

CUT OUT THIS SPACE

CUT

Insert up to
purple line

TAIL
UNDERSIDE

CUT

JEDI
STARFIGHTER

UNDERSIDE

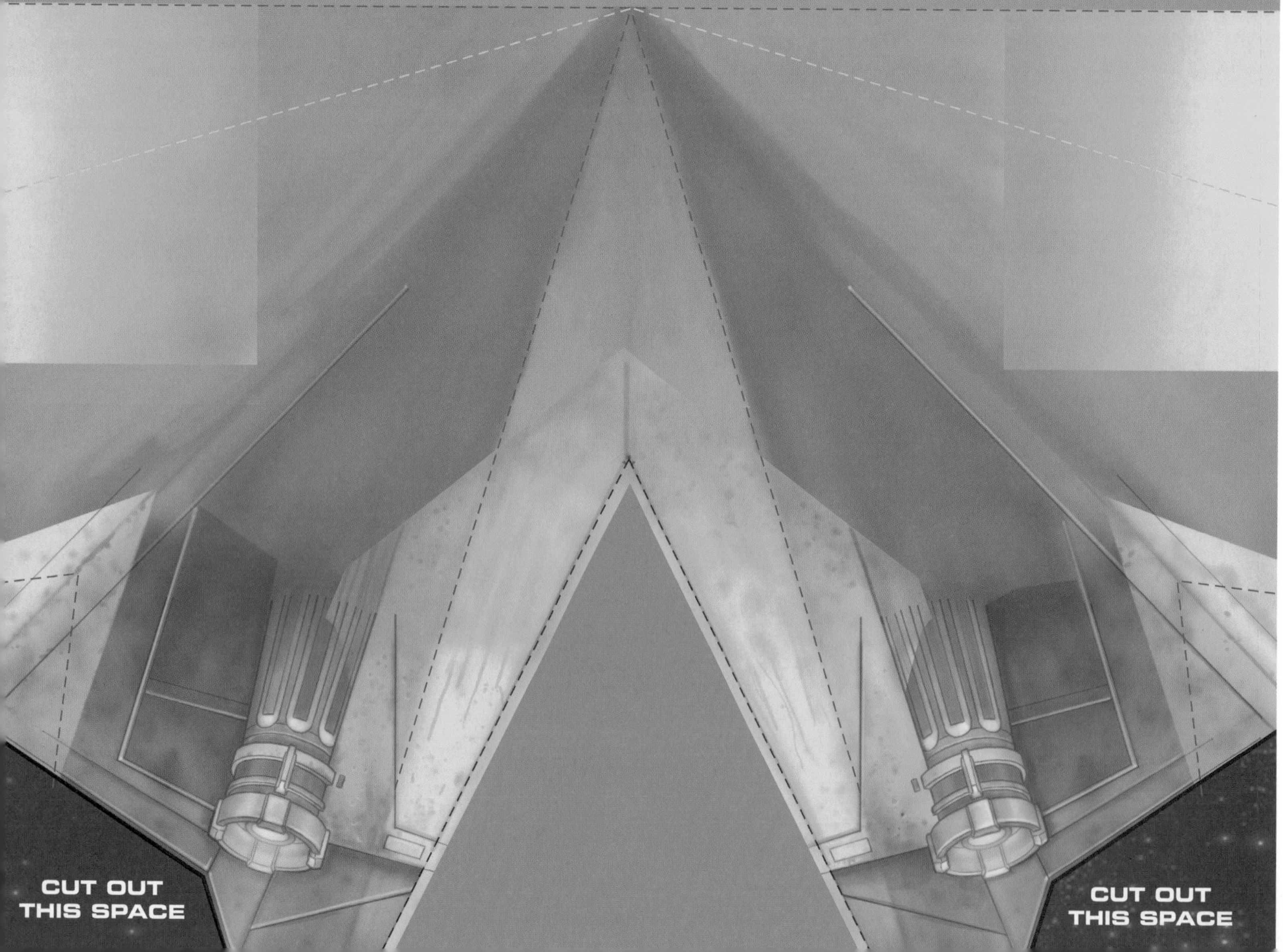

CUT OUT
THIS SPACE

CUT OUT
THIS SPACE

JEDI
STARFIGHTER

TOP SIDE

CUT OUT
THIS SPACE

CUT OUT
THIS SPACE

JEDI
STARFIGHTER

UNDERSIDE

CUT OUT
THIS SPACE

CUT OUT
THIS SPACE

JEDI
STARFIGHTER

UNDERSIDE

CUT OUT
THIS SPACE

CUT OUT
THIS SPACE

**JEDI
STARFIGHTER**

UNDERSIDE

CUT OUT
THIS SPACE

CUT OUT
THIS SPACE

JEDI
STARFIGHTER

UNDERSIDE

CUT OUT
THIS SPACE

CUT OUT
THIS SPACE

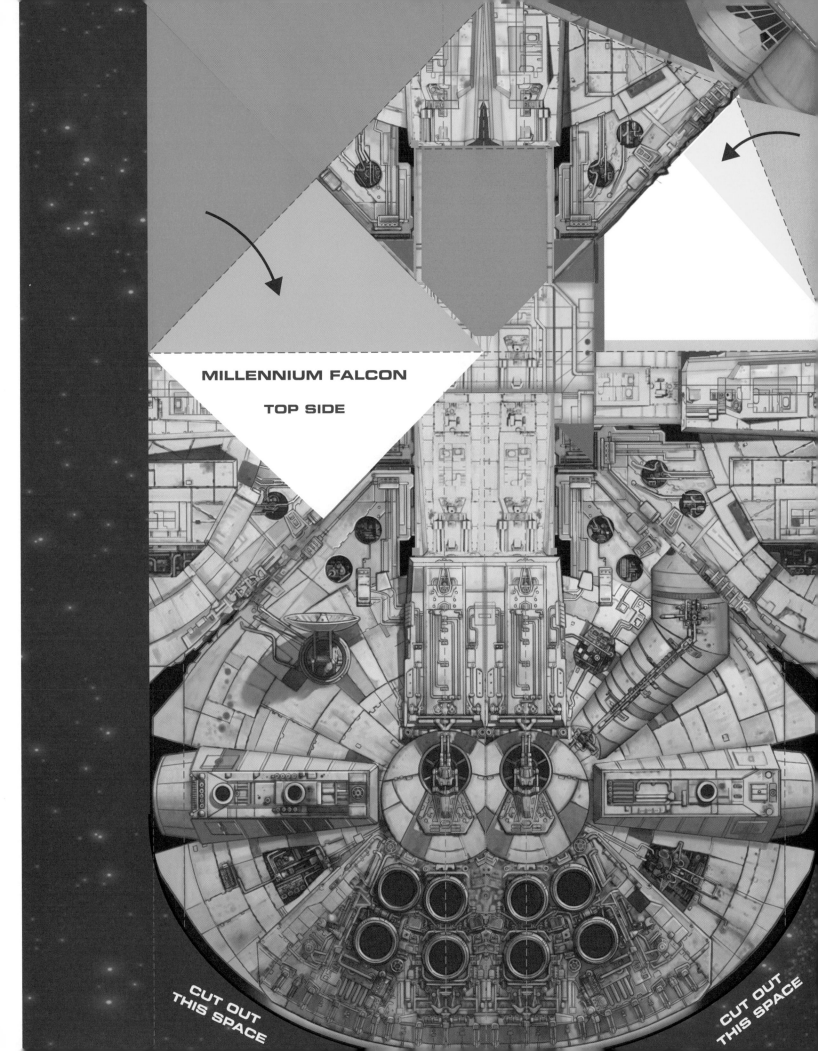

MILLENNIUM FALCON

TOP SIDE

CUT OUT
THIS SPACE

CUT OUT
THIS SPACE

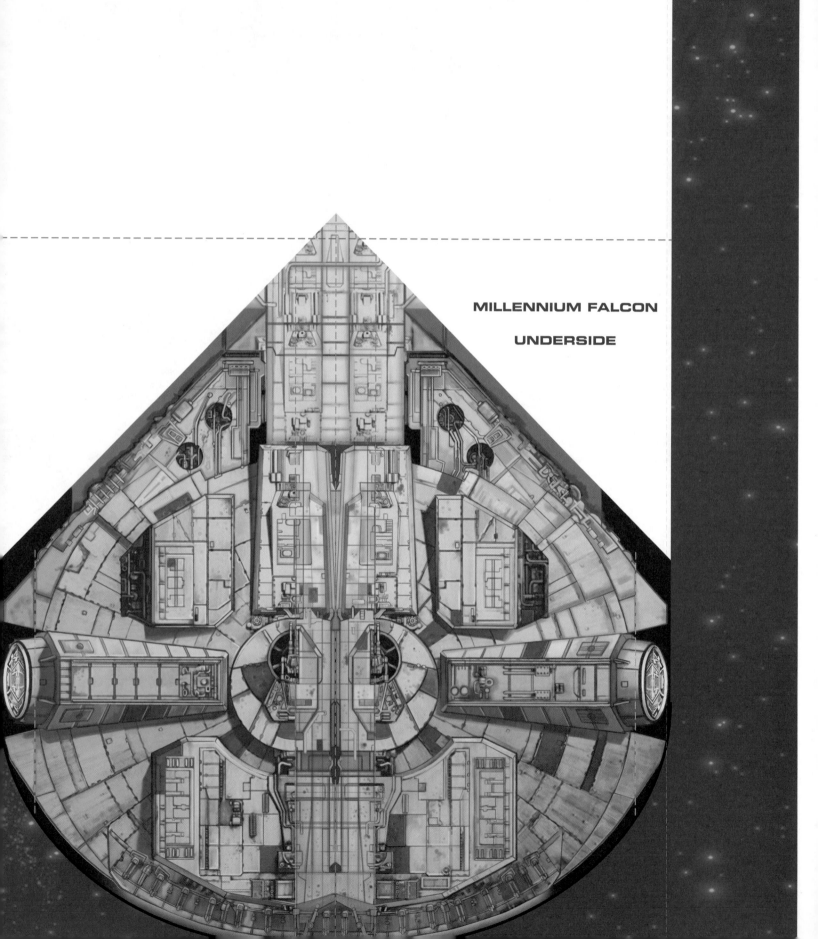

MILLENNIUM FALCON

UNDERSIDE

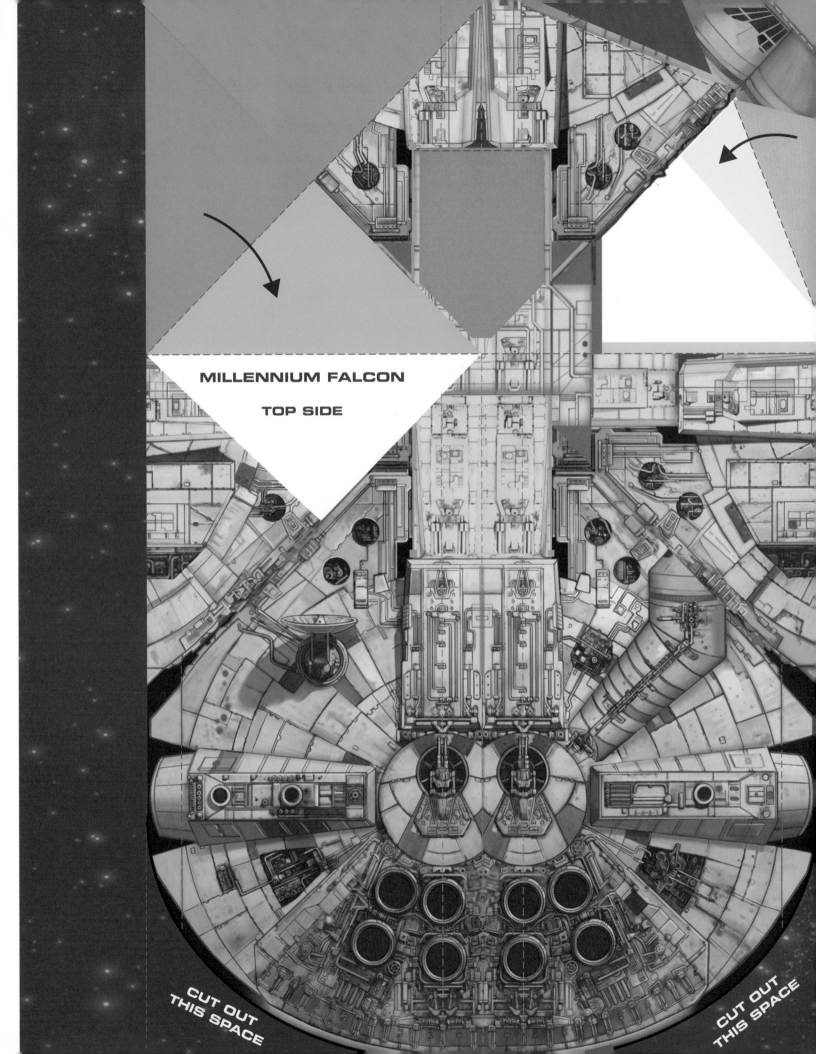

MILLENNIUM FALCON

TOP SIDE

CUT OUT
THIS SPACE

CUT OUT
THIS SPACE

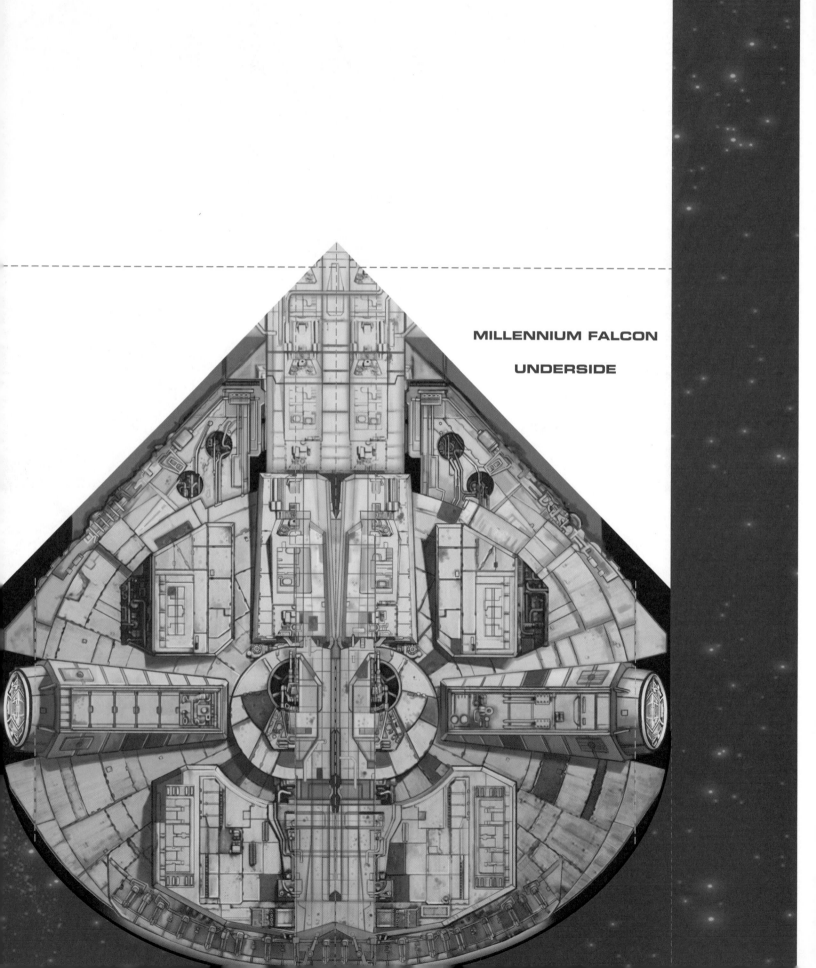

MILLENNIUM FALCON

UNDERSIDE

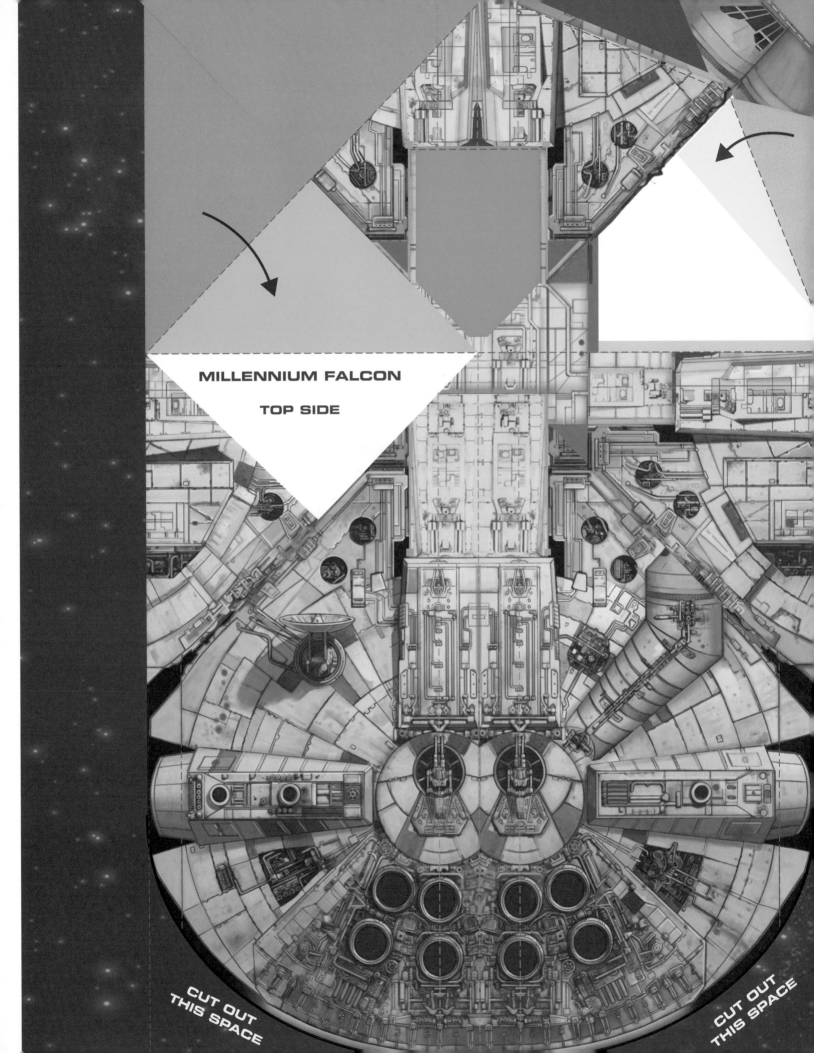

MILLENNIUM FALCON

TOP SIDE

CUT OUT
THIS SPACE

CUT OUT
THIS SPACE

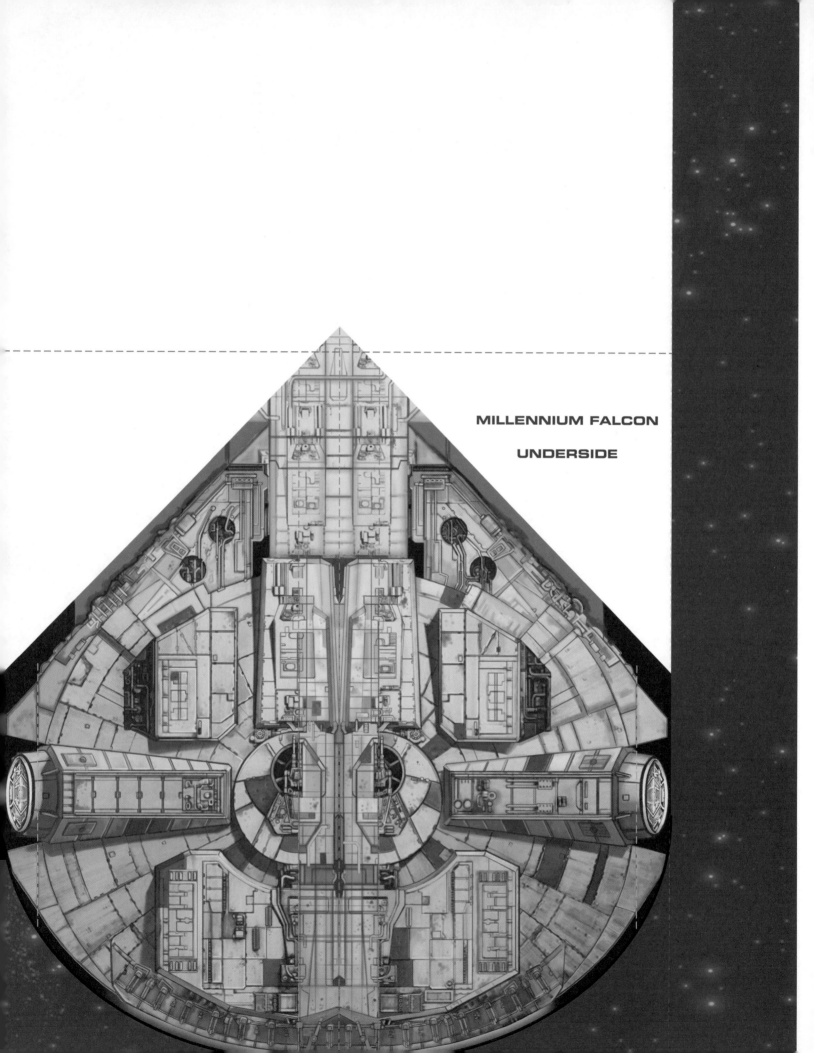

MILLENNIUM FALCON

UNDERSIDE

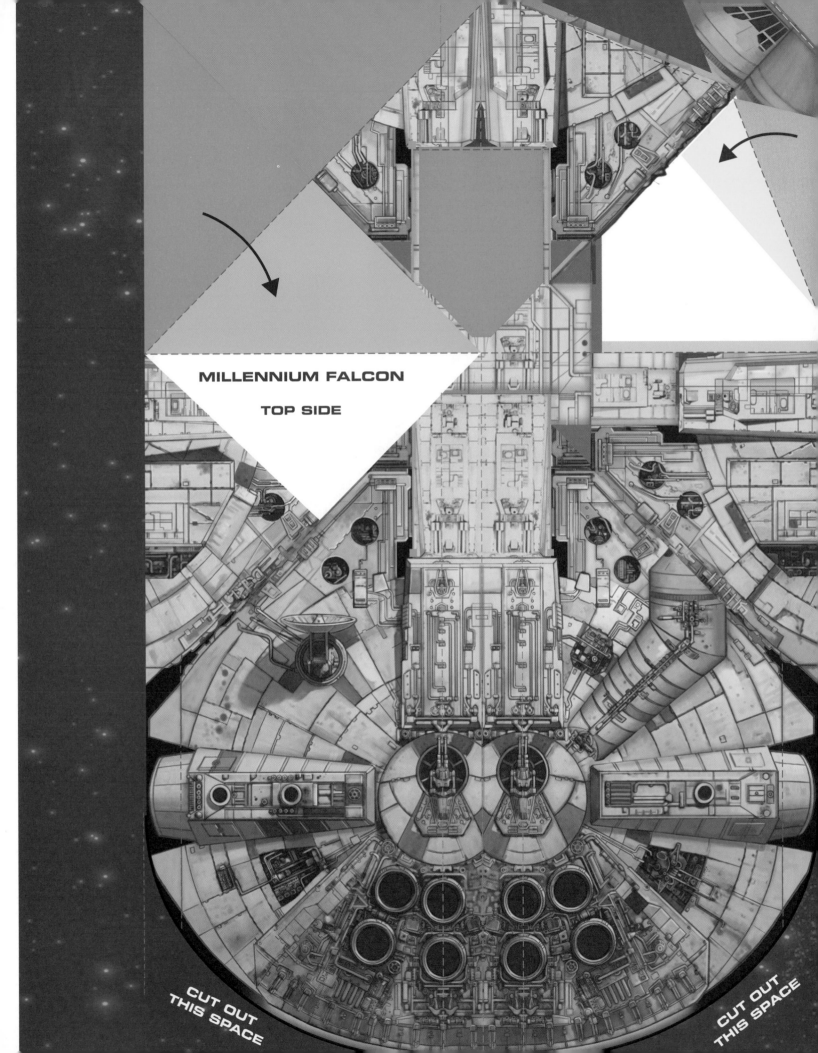

MILLENNIUM FALCON

TOP SIDE

CUT OUT
THIS SPACE

CUT OUT
THIS SPACE

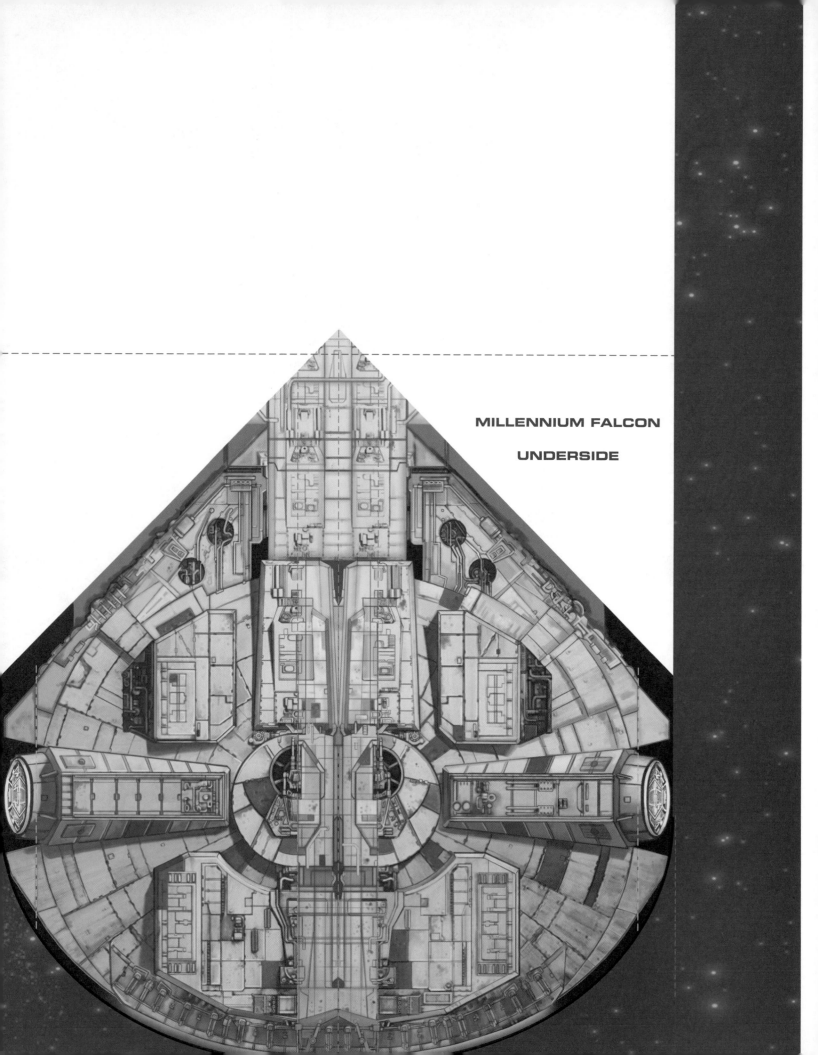

MILLENNIUM FALCON

UNDERSIDE

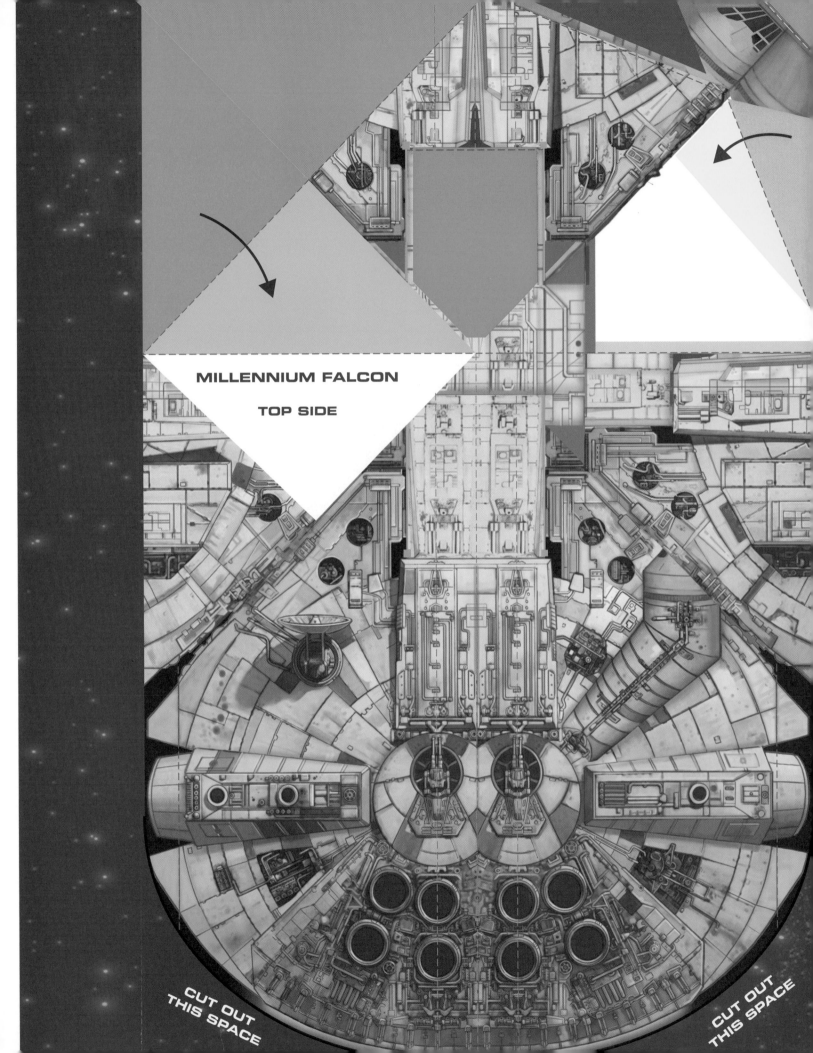

MILLENNIUM FALCON

TOP SIDE

CUT OUT
THIS SPACE

CUT OUT
THIS SPACE

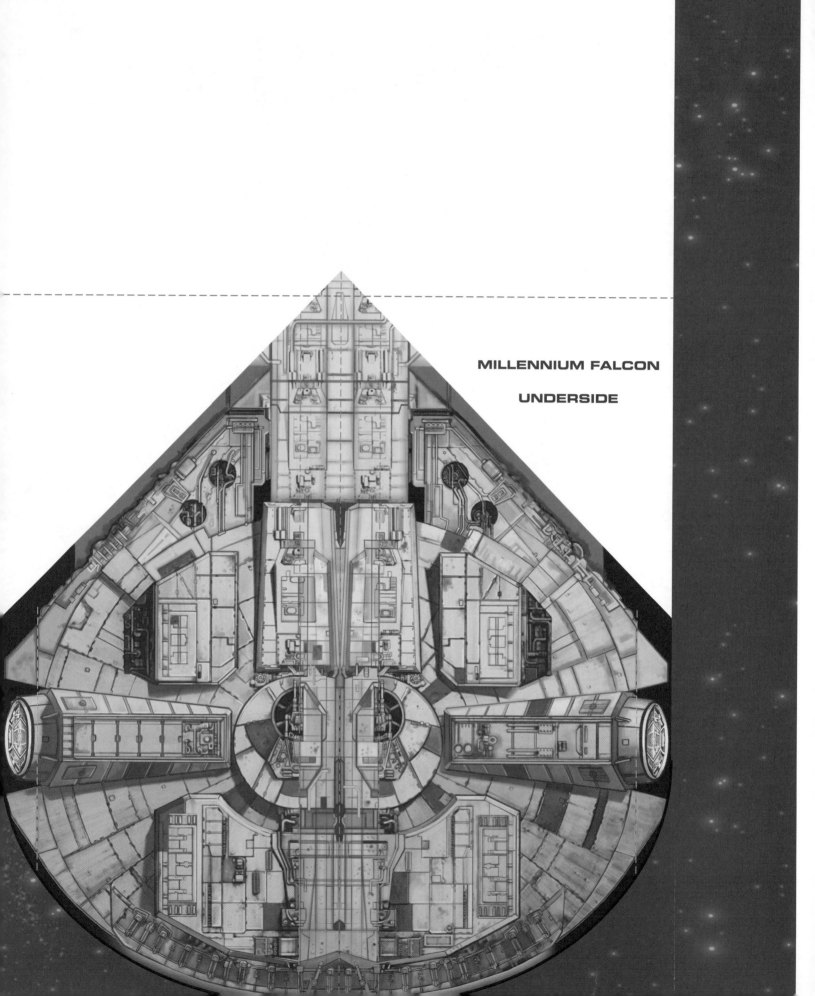

MILLENNIUM FALCON

UNDERSIDE

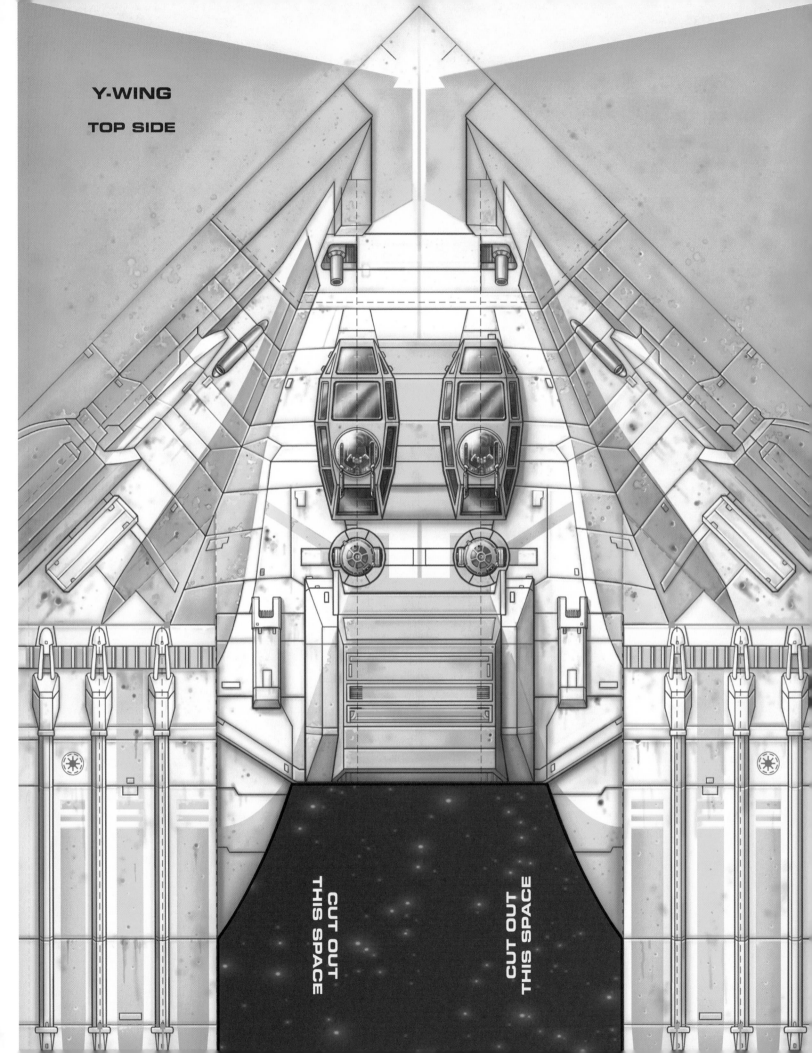

Y-WING

UNDERSIDE

CUT OUT THIS SPACE

CUT OUT THIS SPACE

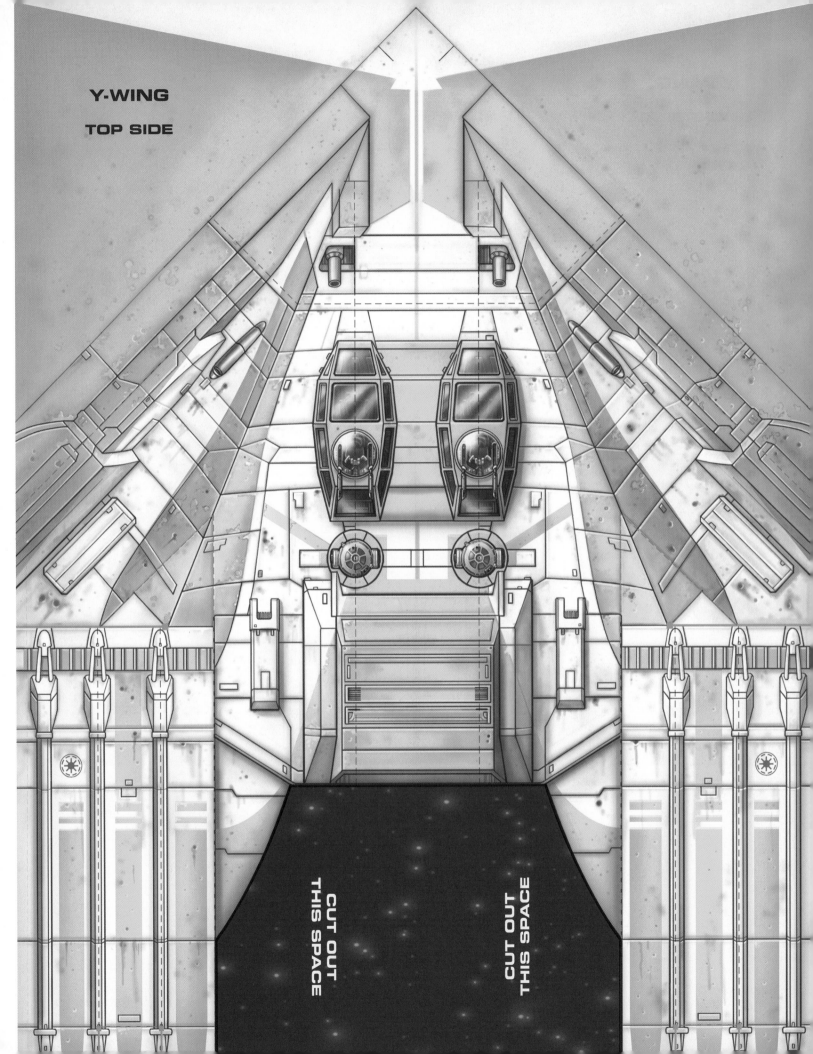

Y-WING

TOP SIDE

CUT OUT THIS SPACE

CUT OUT THIS SPACE

Y-WING

UNDERSIDE

CUT OUT THIS SPACE

CUT OUT THIS SPACE

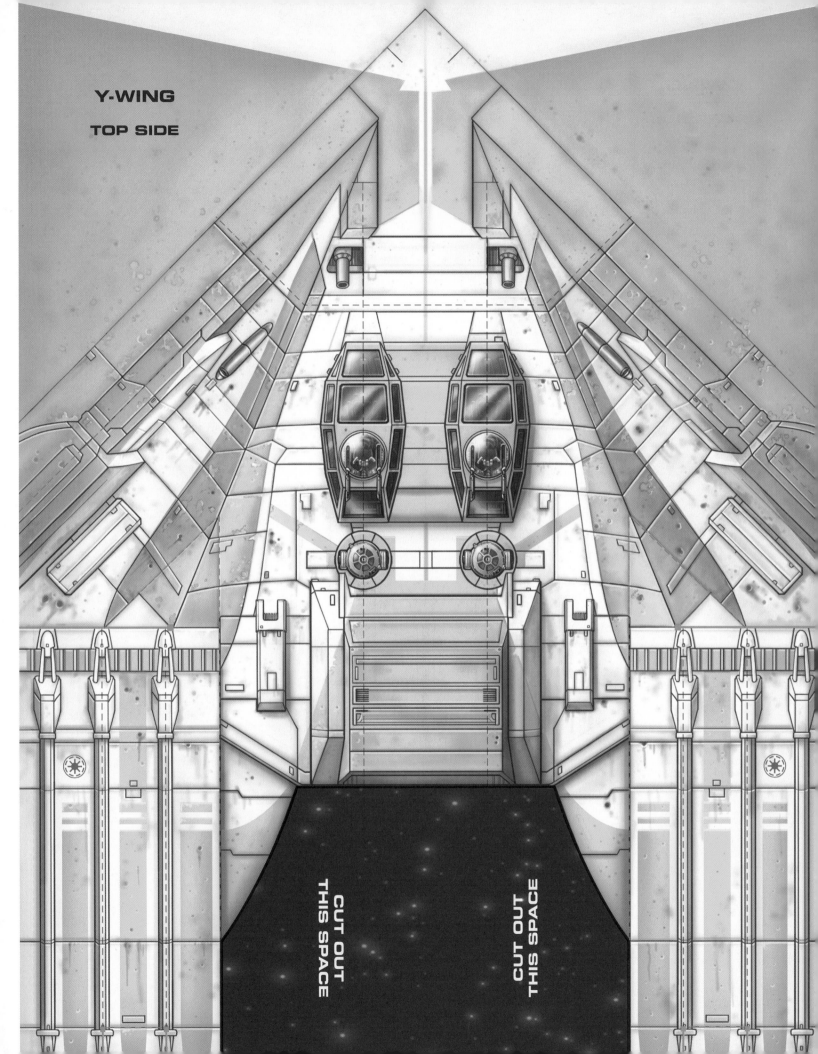

Y-WING

TOP SIDE

CUT OUT THIS SPACE

CUT OUT THIS SPACE

Y-WING

UNDERSIDE

CUT OUT
THIS SPACE

CUT OUT
THIS SPACE

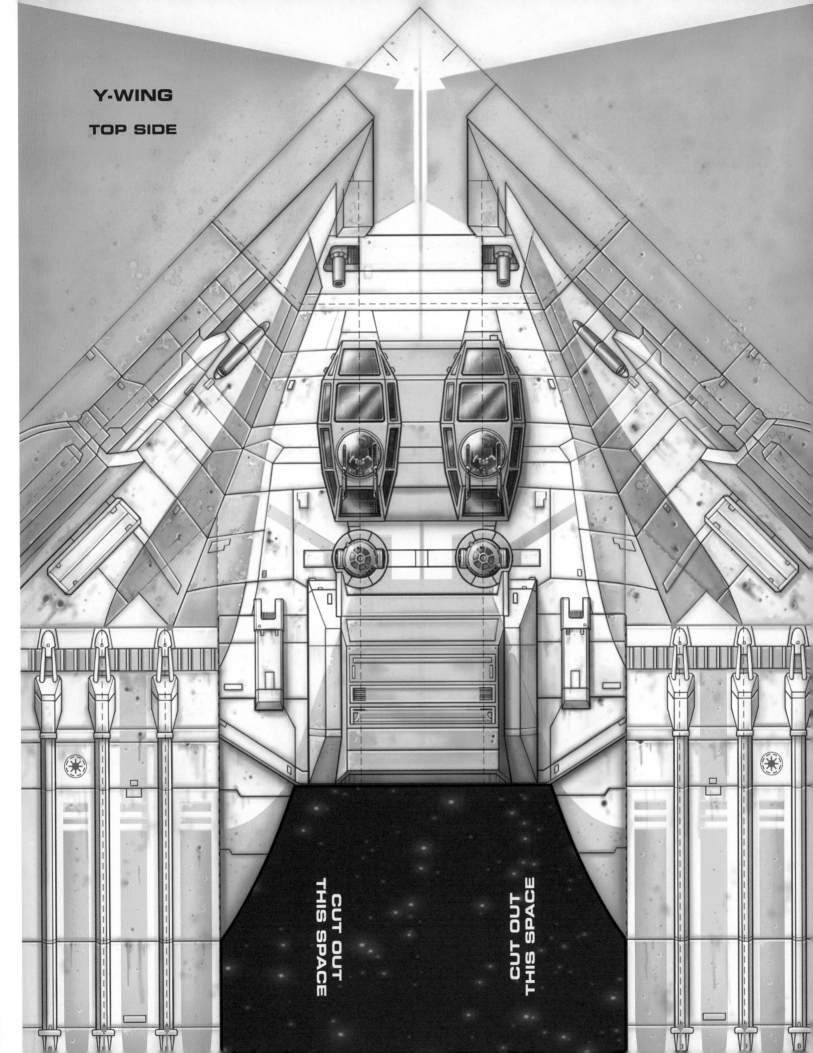

Y-WING

UNDERSIDE

CUT OUT
THIS SPACE

CUT OUT
THIS SPACE

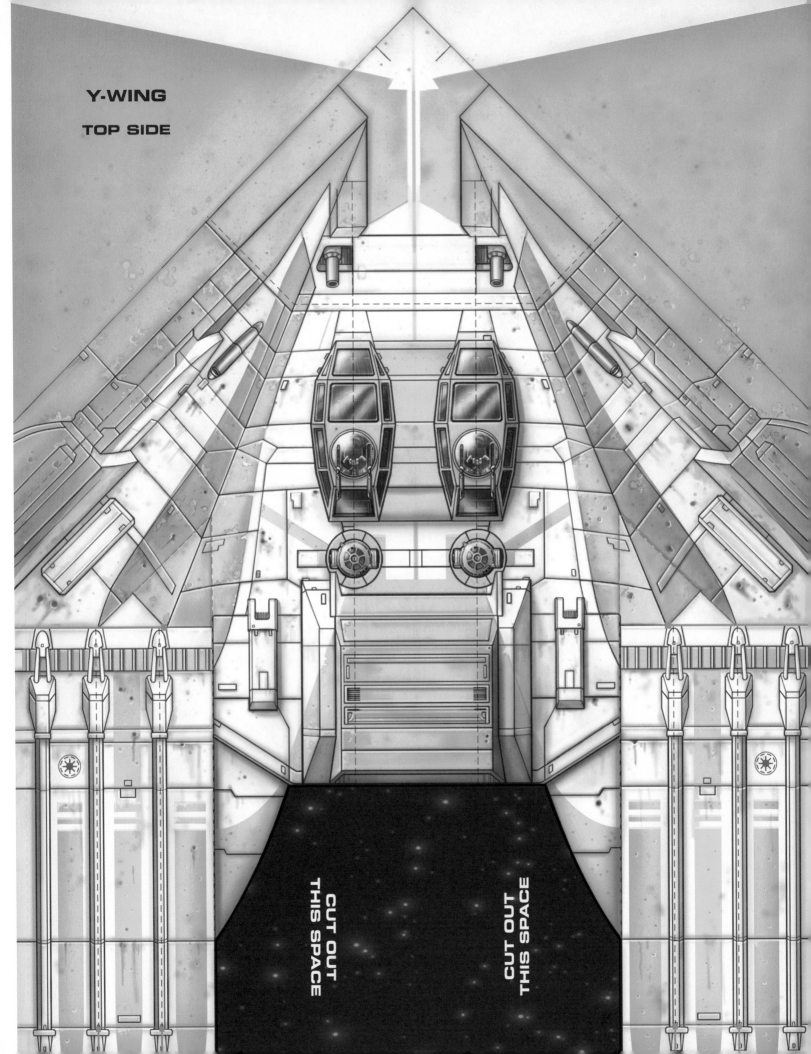

Y-WING

TOP SIDE

CUT OUT
THIS SPACE

CUT OUT
THIS SPACE

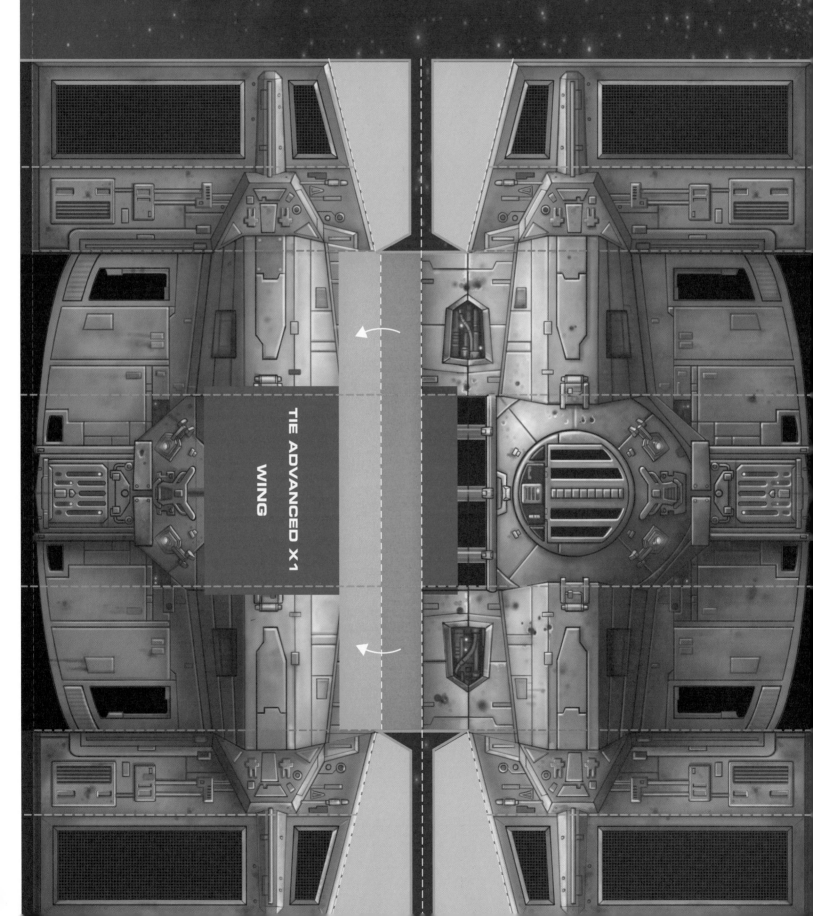

CUT OFF THIS SPACE

TIE ADVANCED X1
WING

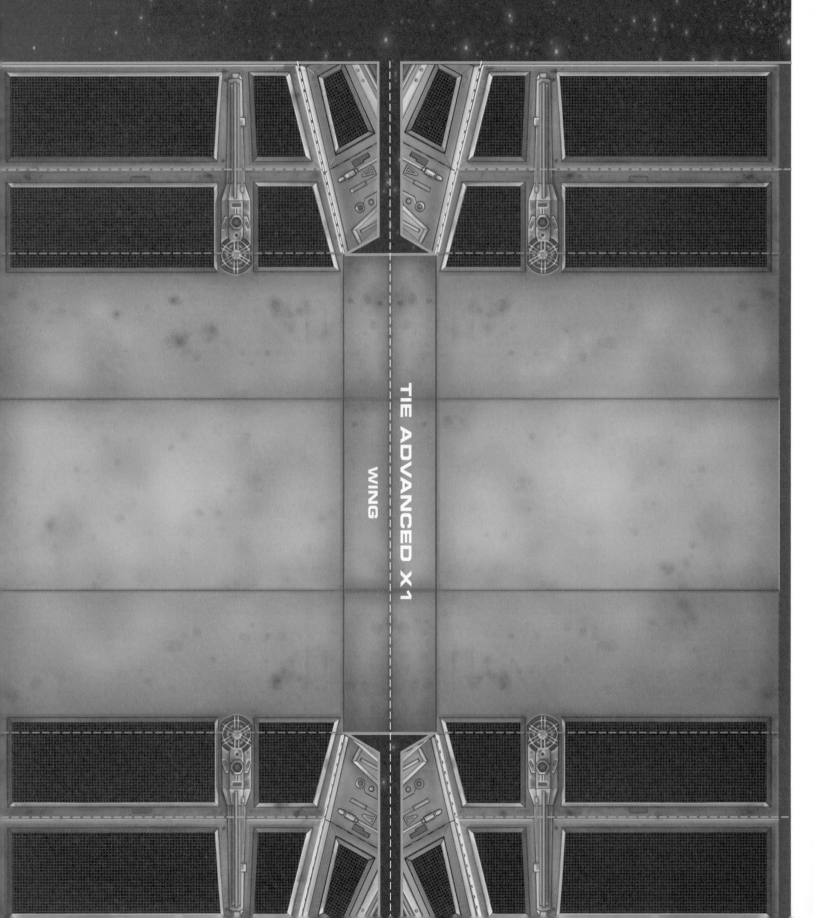

CUT OFF THIS SPACE

TIE ADVANCED X1

WING

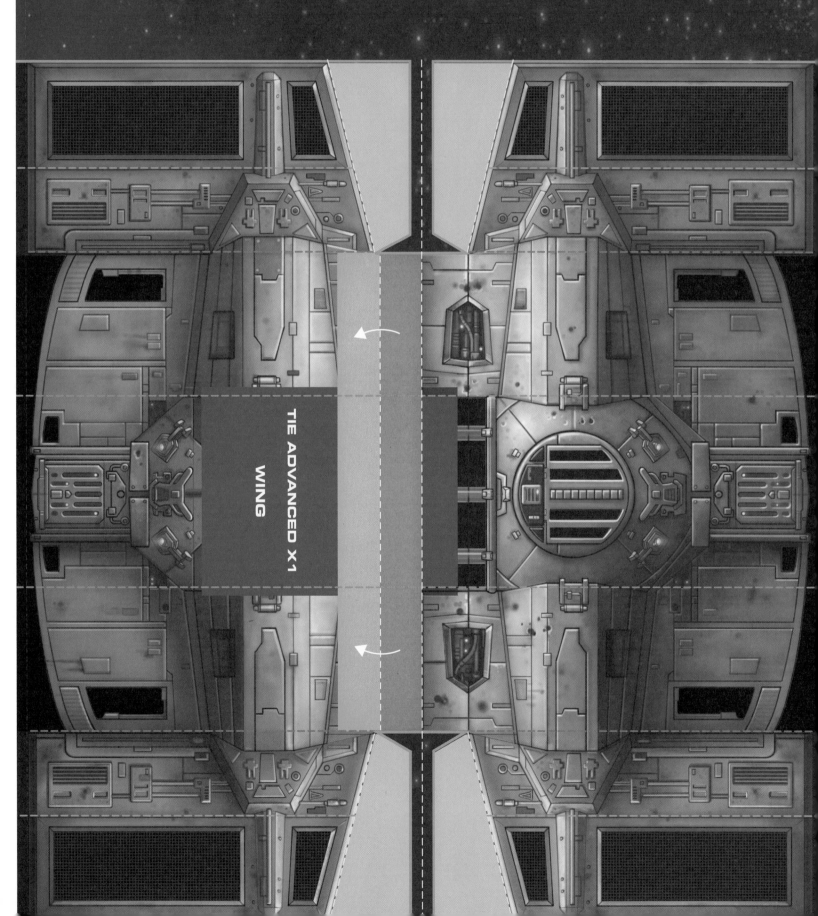

CUT OFF THIS SPACE

TIE ADVANCED X1
WING

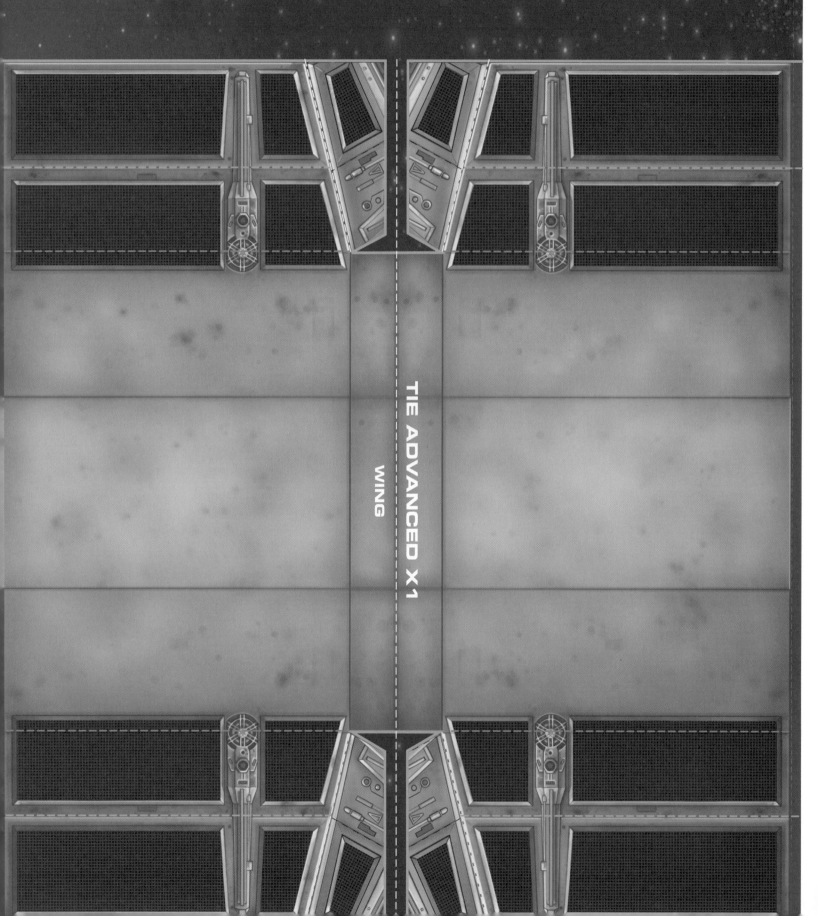

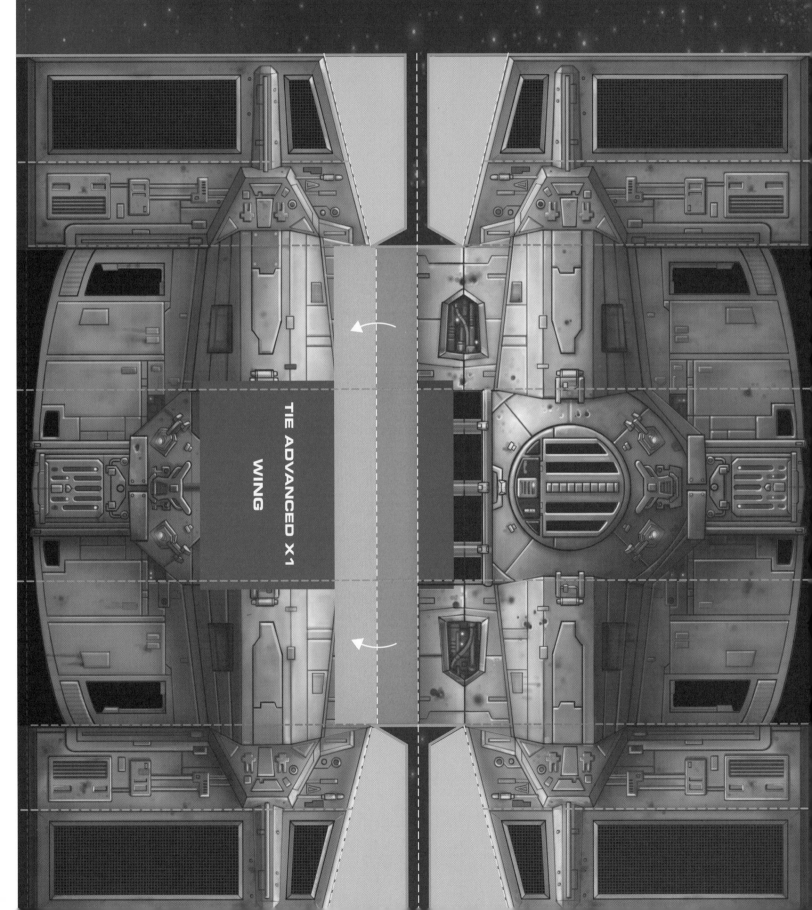

TIE ADVANCED X1
WING

CUT OFF THIS SPACE

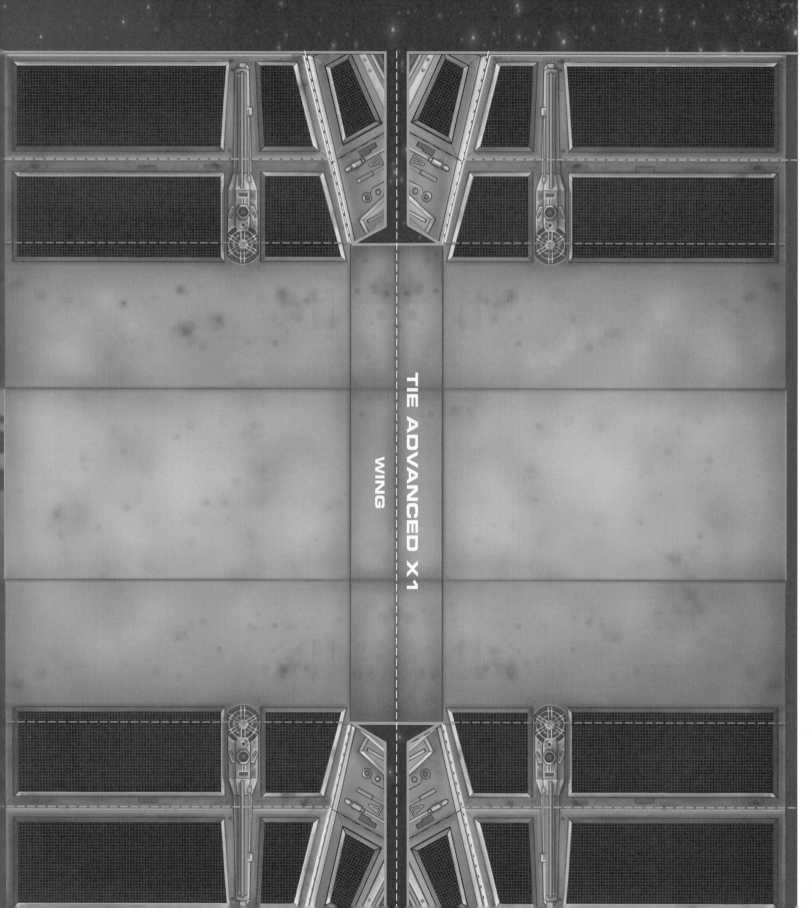

TIE ADVANCED X1

WING

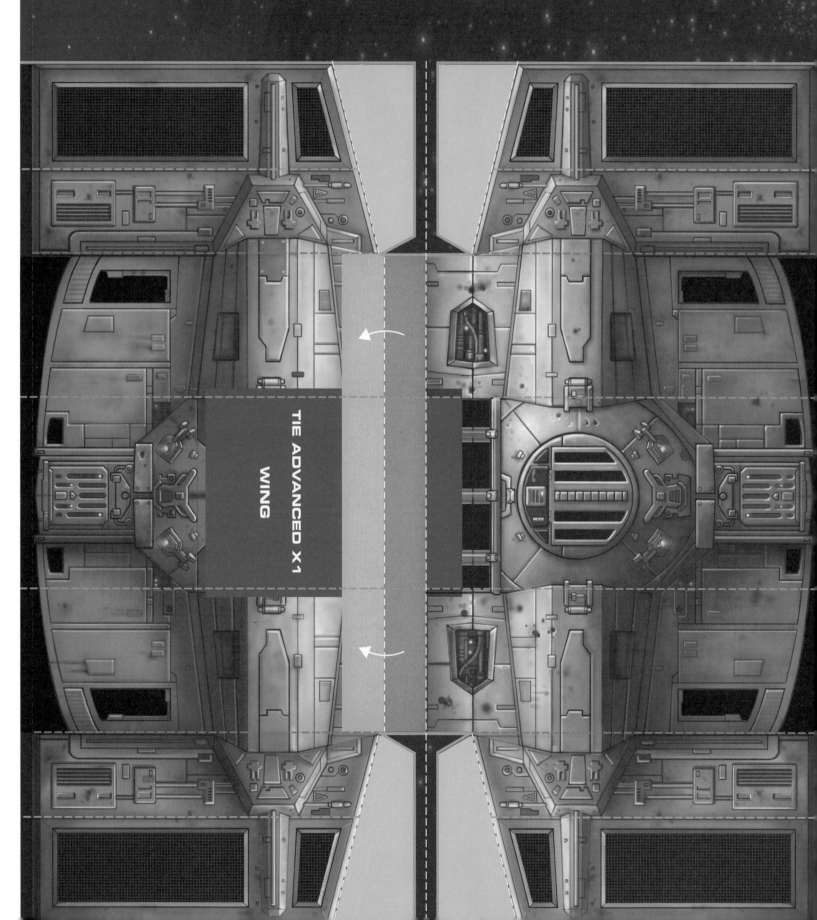

TIE ADVANCED X1

WING

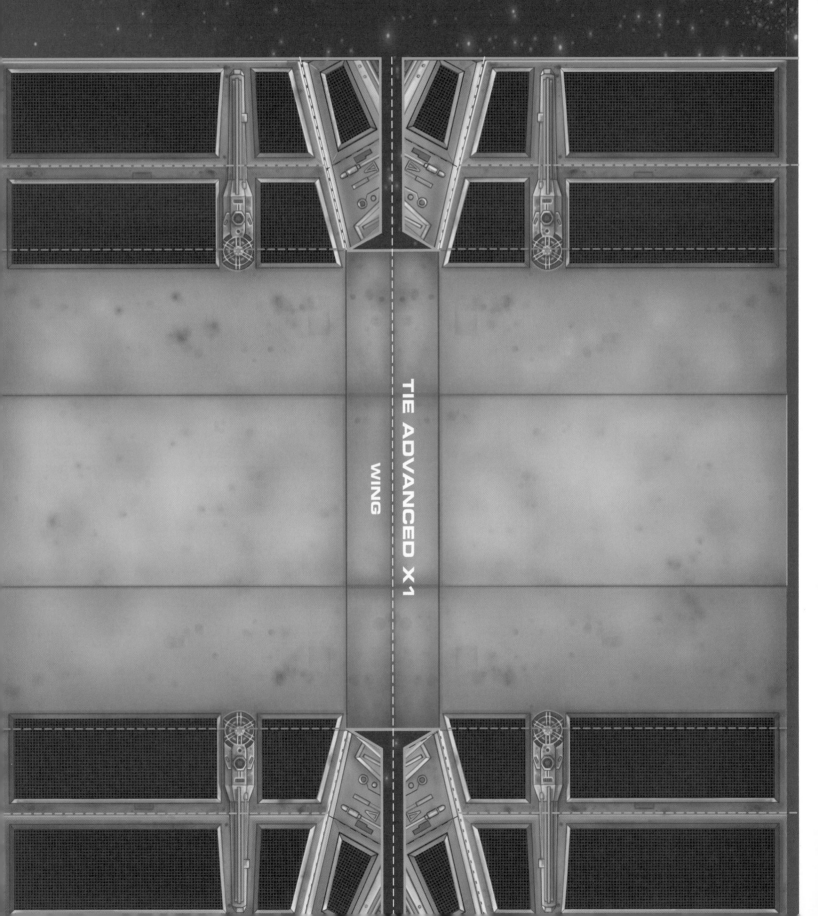

TIE ADVANCED X1

WING

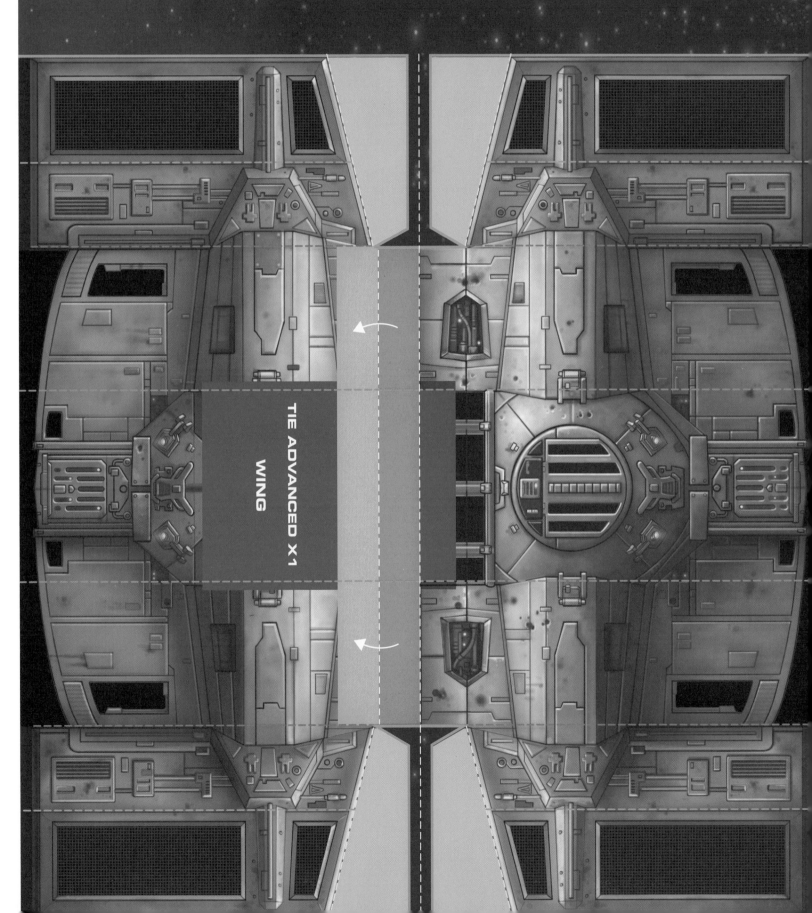

TIE ADVANCED X1
WING

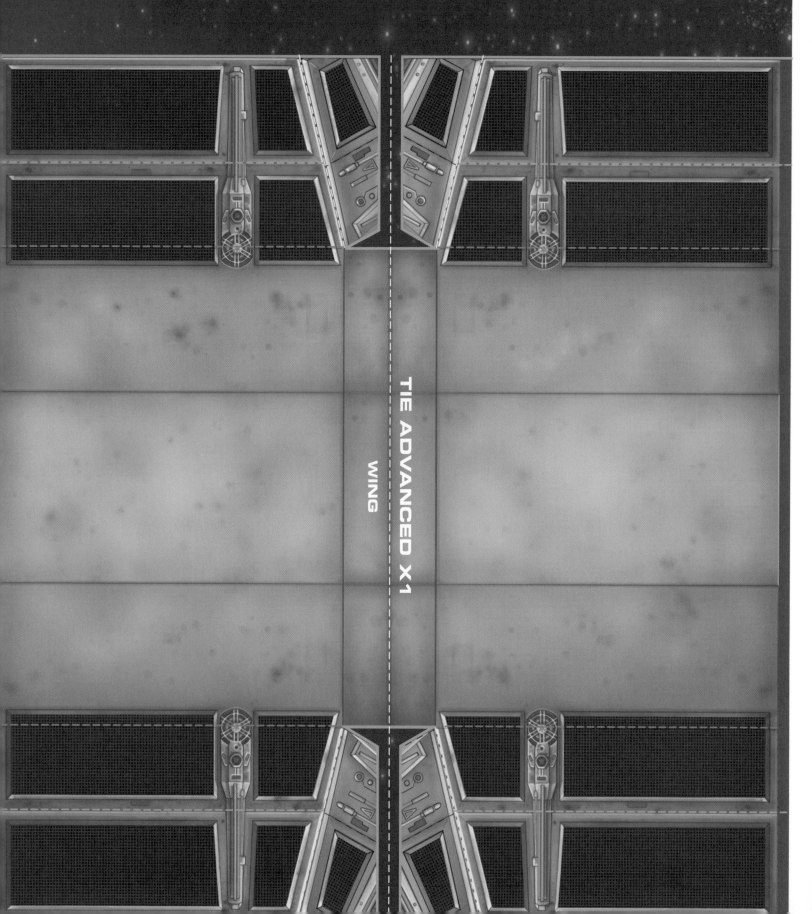

CUT OFF THIS SPACE

TIE ADVANCED X1

WIING

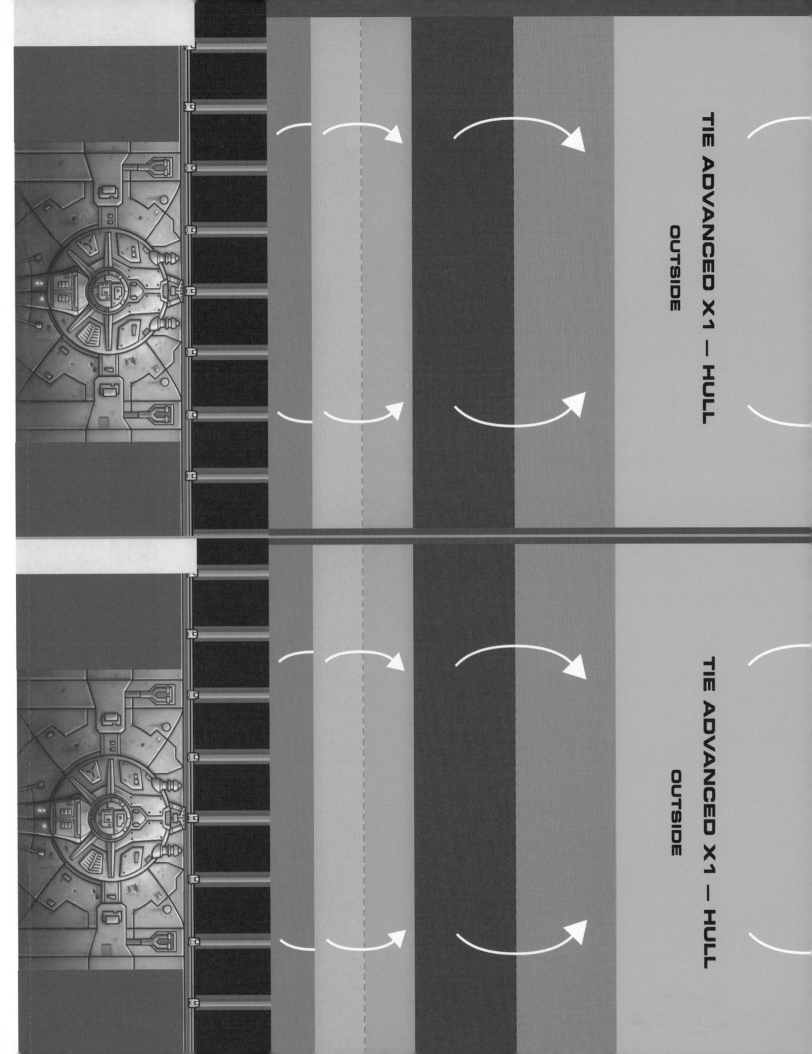

TIE ADVANCED X1 — HULL

OUTSIDE

TIE ADVANCED X1 — HULL

OUTSIDE

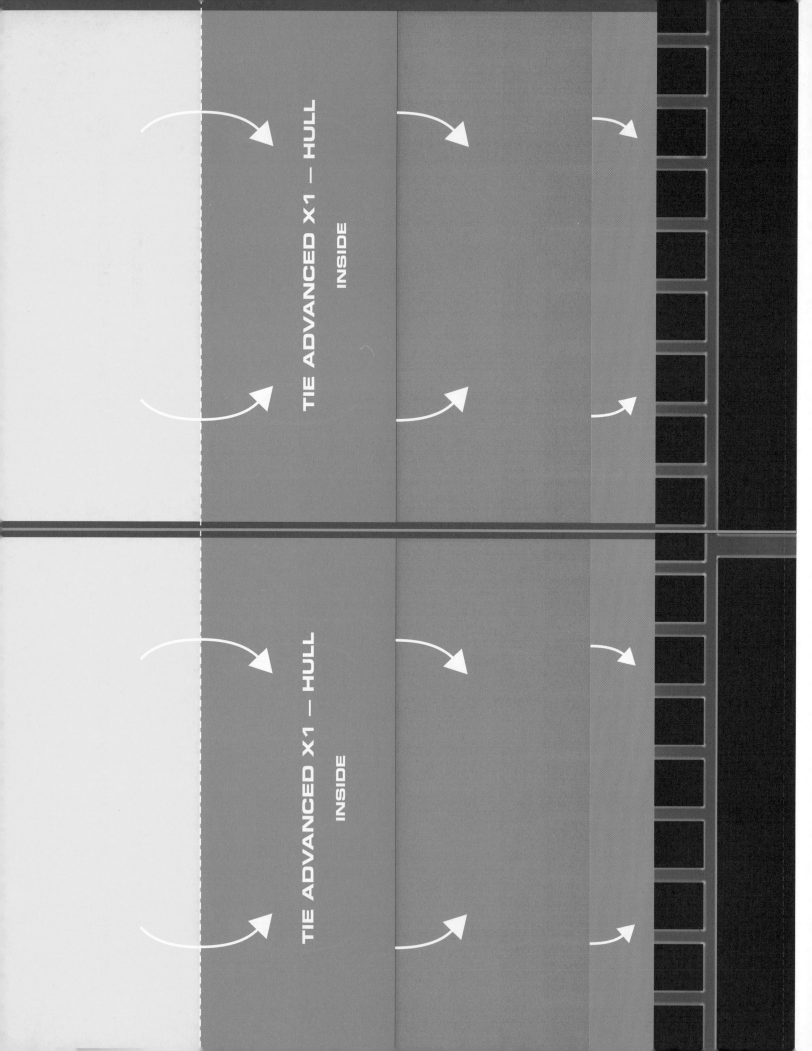

TIE ADVANCED X1 — HULL

INSIDE

TIE ADVANCED X1 — HULL

INSIDE

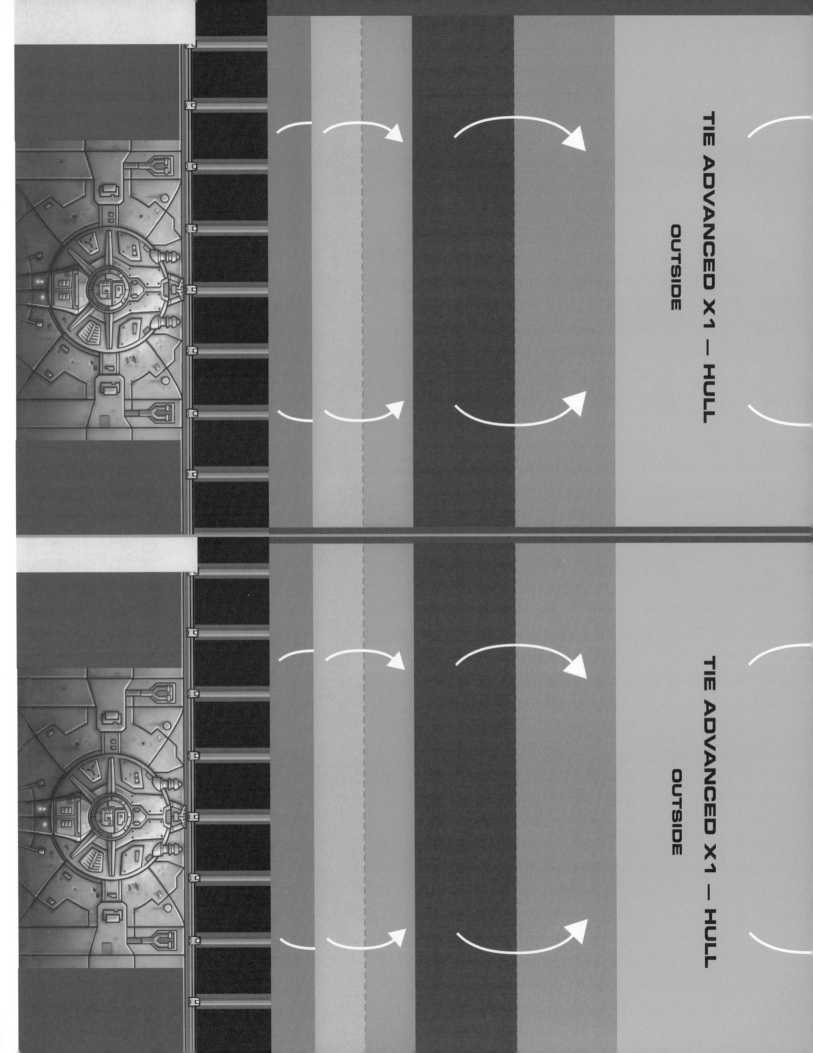

TIE ADVANCED X1 — HULL

OUTSIDE

TIE ADVANCED X1 — HULL

OUTSIDE

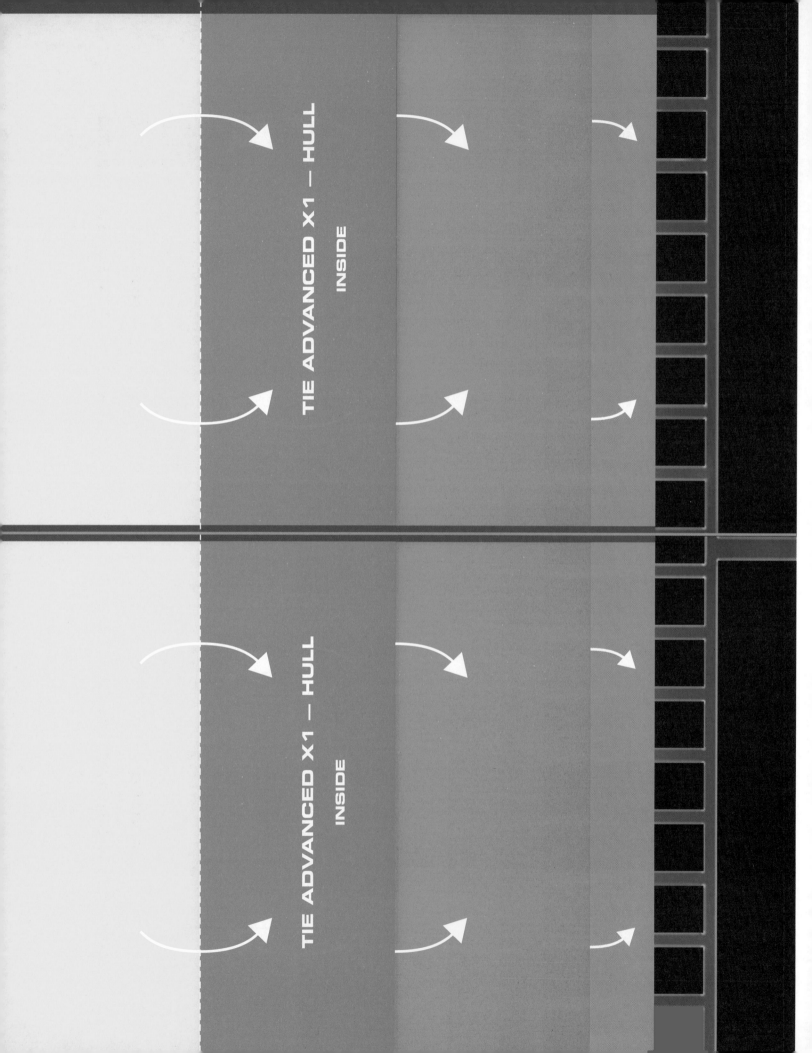

TIE ADVANCED X1 — HULL

INSIDE

TIE ADVANCED X1 — HULL

INSIDE

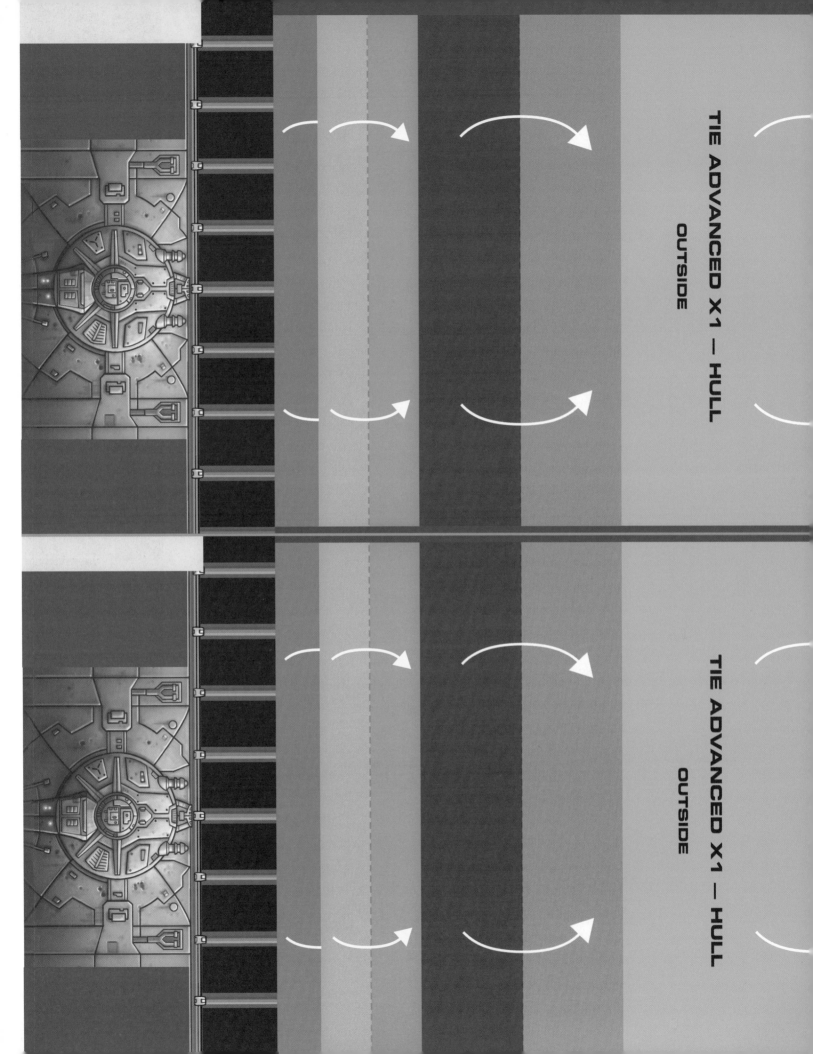

TIE ADVANCED X1 — HULL

OUTSIDE

TIE ADVANCED X1 — HULL

OUTSIDE

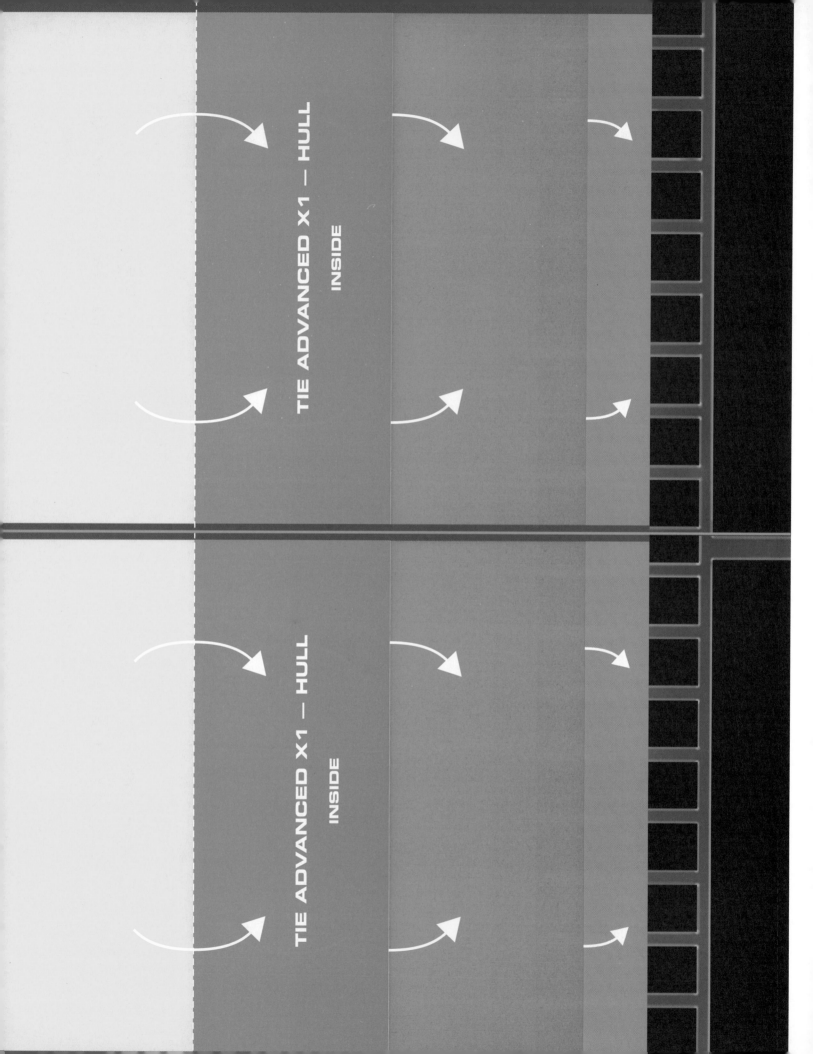

TIE ADVANCED X1 — HULL

INSIDE

TIE ADVANCED X1 — HULL

INSIDE

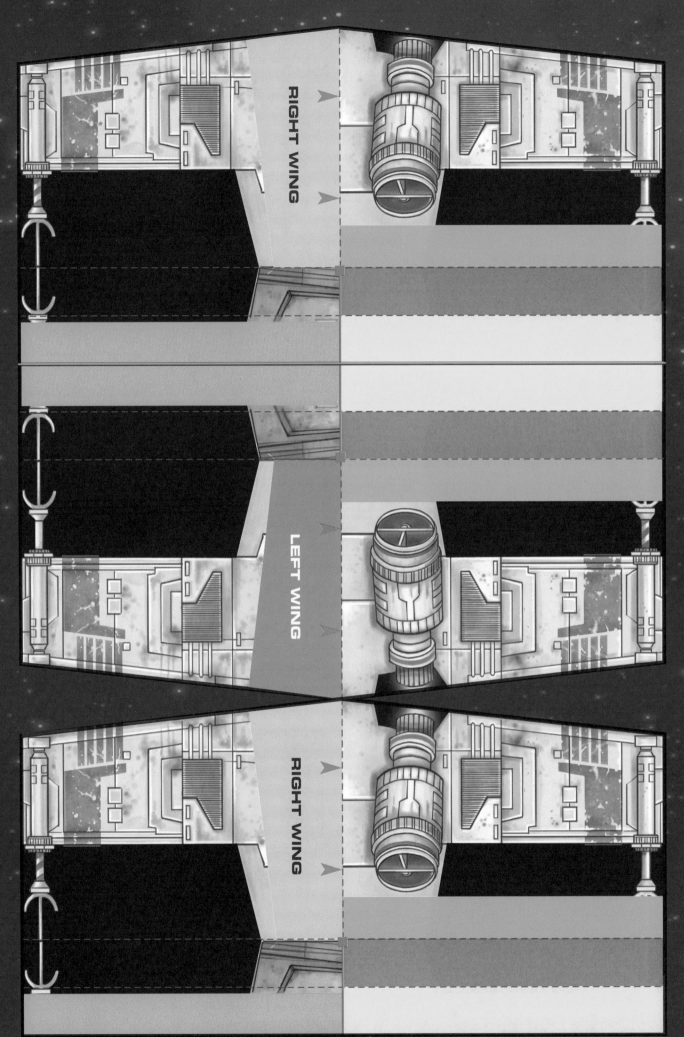

X-WING — WINGS (RIGHT, LEFT, RIGHT)

RIGHT WING

LEFT WING

RIGHT WING

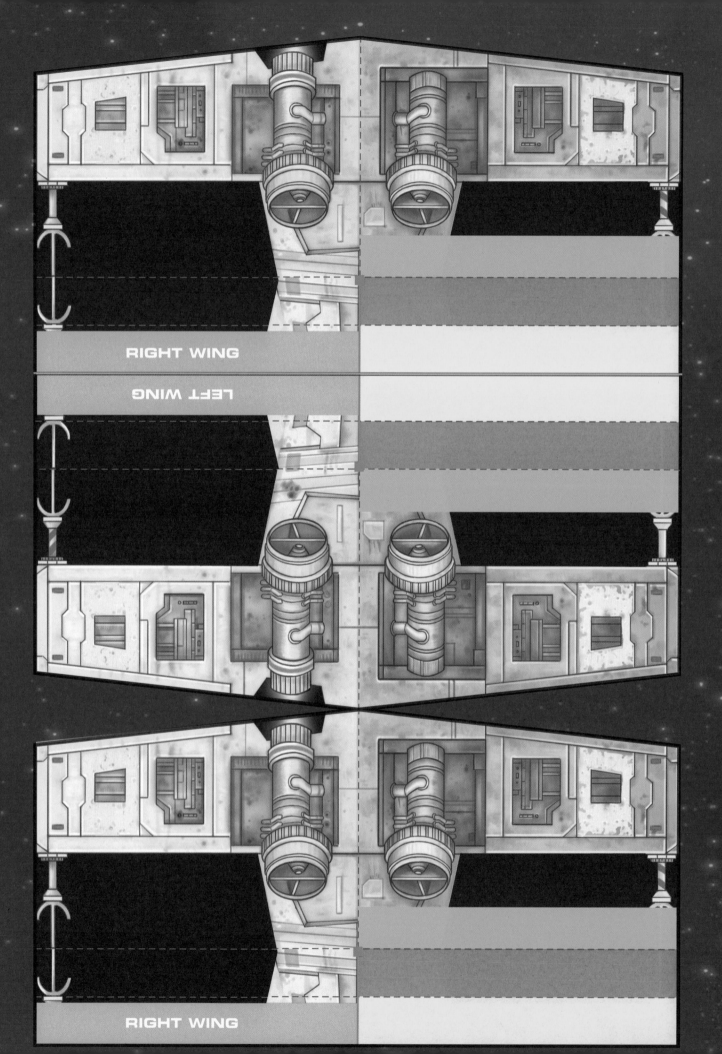

RIGHT WING

LEFT WING

RIGHT WING

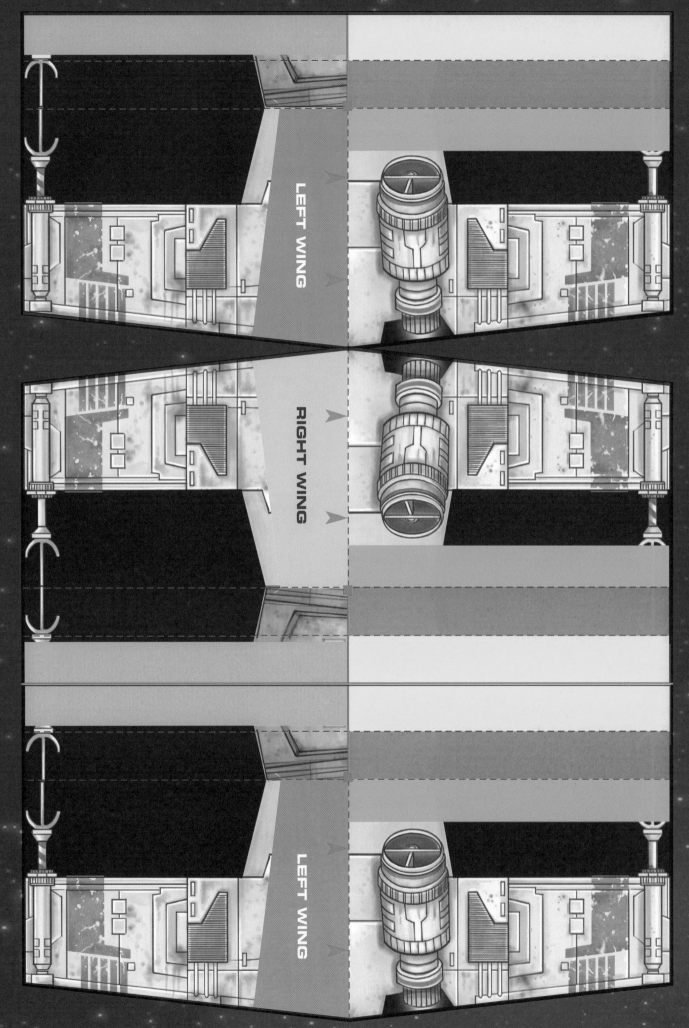

LEFT WING

RIGHT WING

LEFT WING

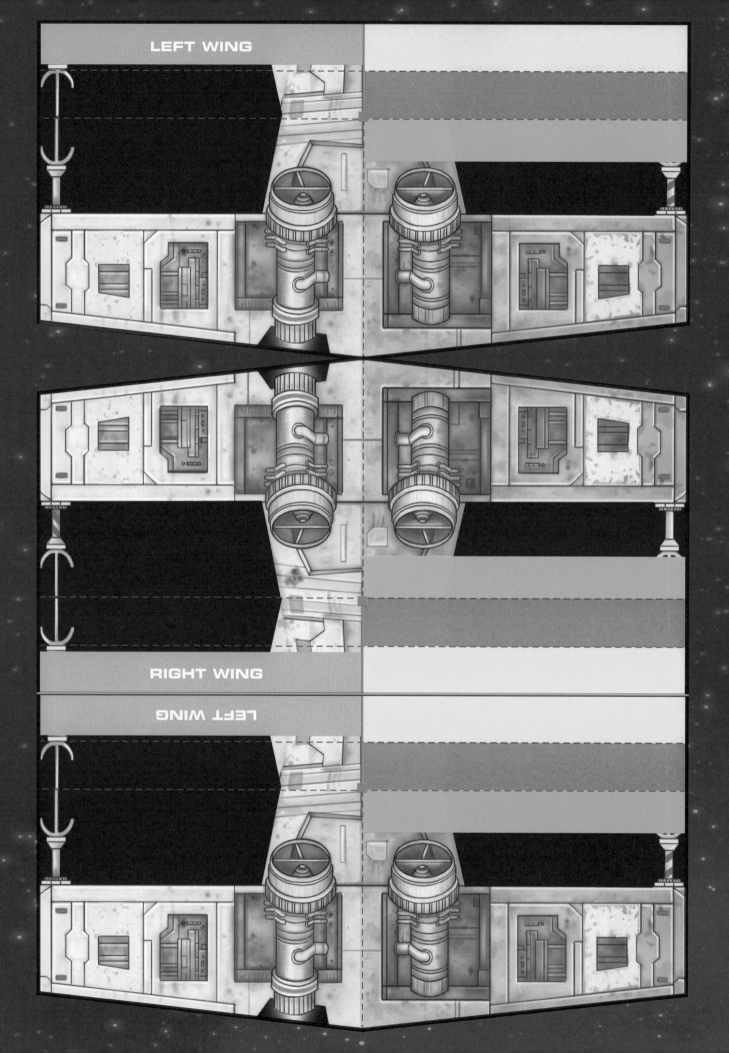

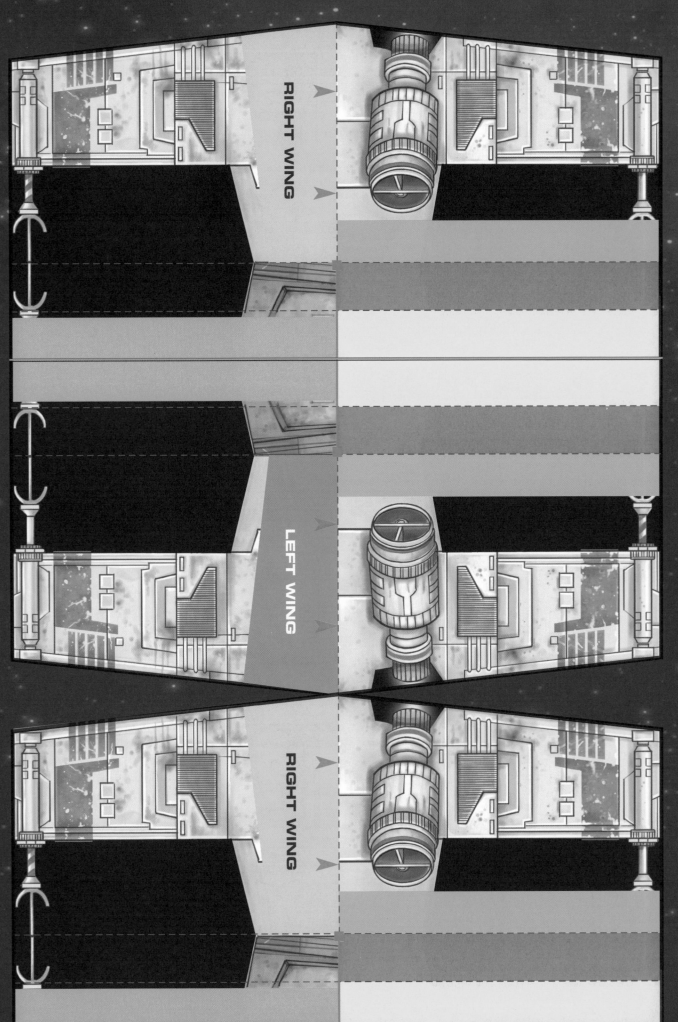

RIGHT WING

LEFT WING

RIGHT WING

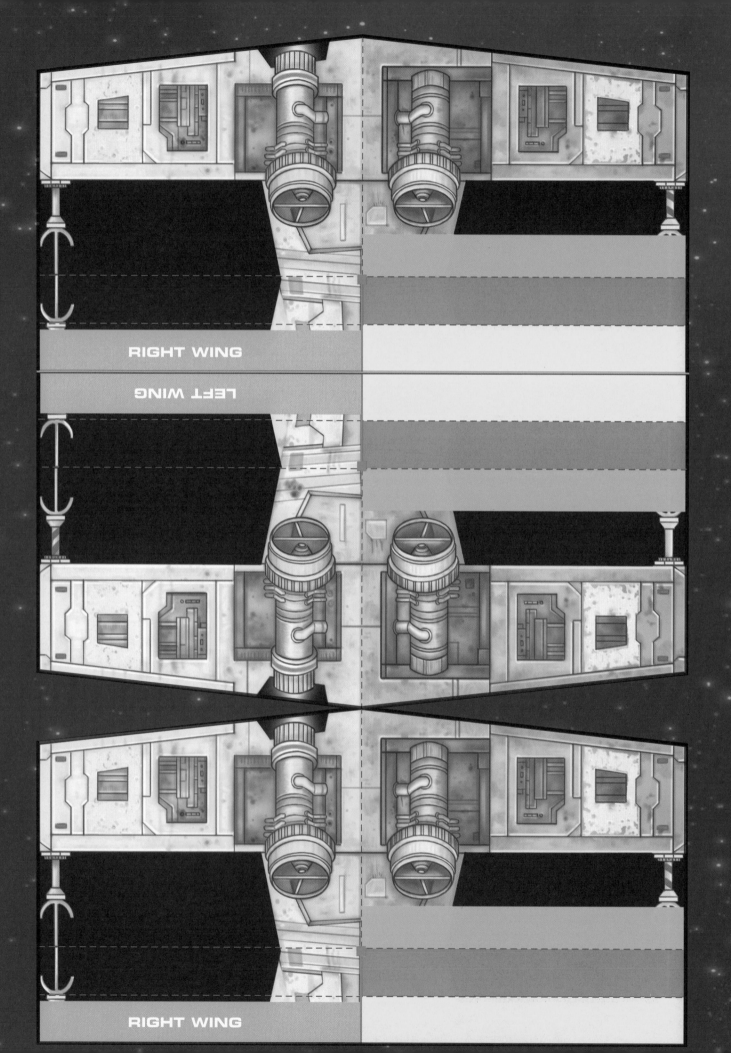

RIGHT WING

LEFT WING

RIGHT WING

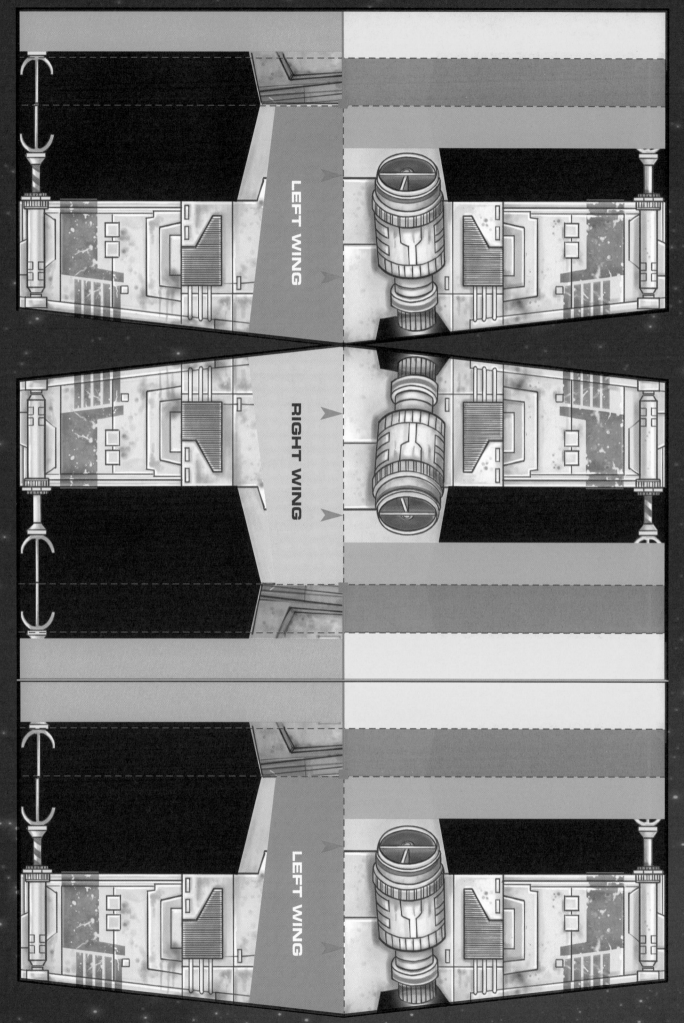

LEFT WING

RIGHT WING

LEFT WING

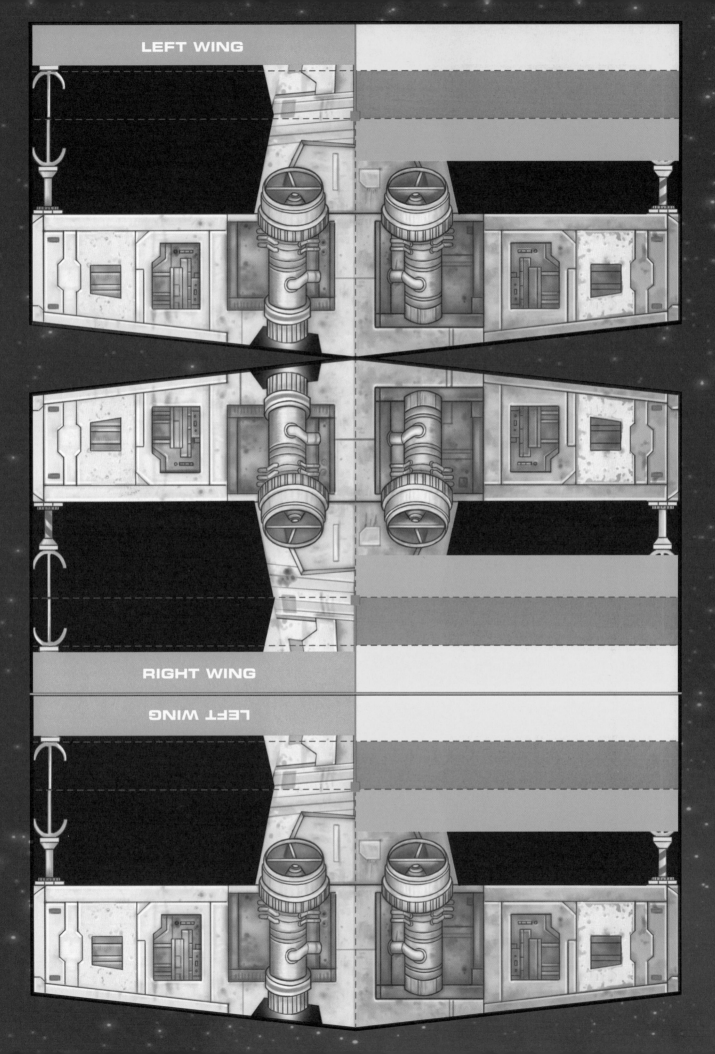

LEFT WING

RIGHT WING

LEFT WING

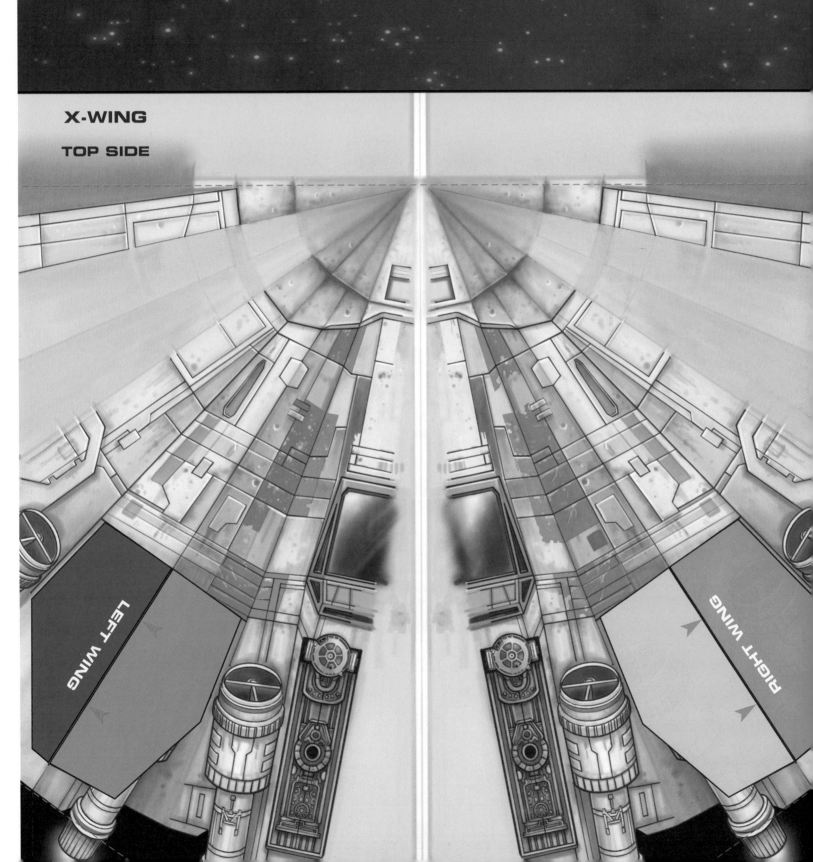

CUT OFF THIS SPACE

X-WING

TOP SIDE

LEFT WING

RIGHT WING

CUT OFF THIS SPACE

X-WING

UNDERSIDE

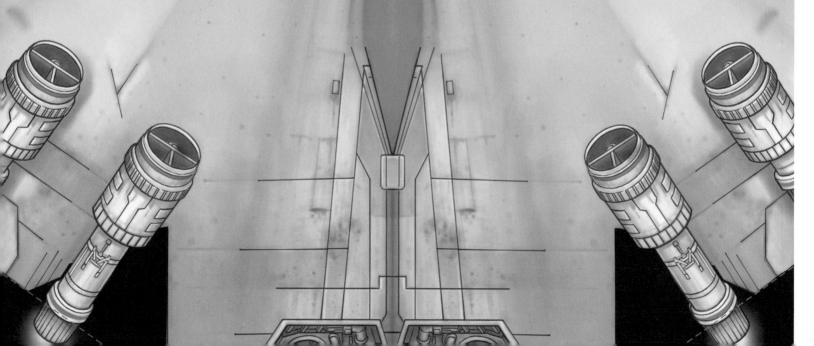

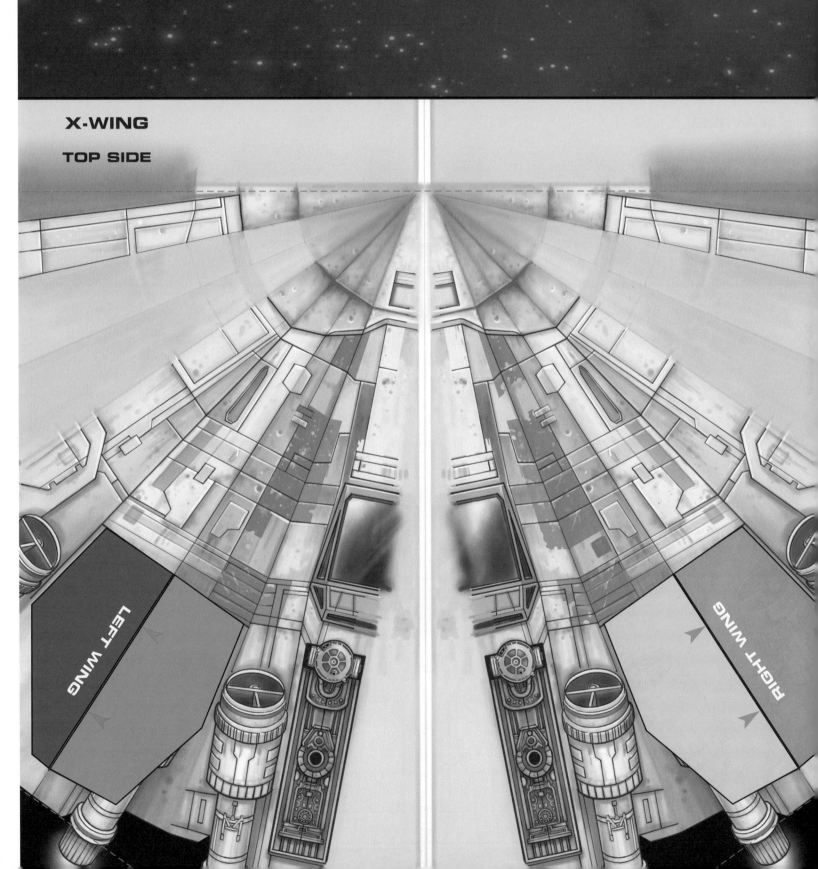

CUT OFF THIS SPACE

X-WING

TOP SIDE

LEFT WING

RIGHT WING

CUT OFF THIS SPACE

X-WING

UNDERSIDE

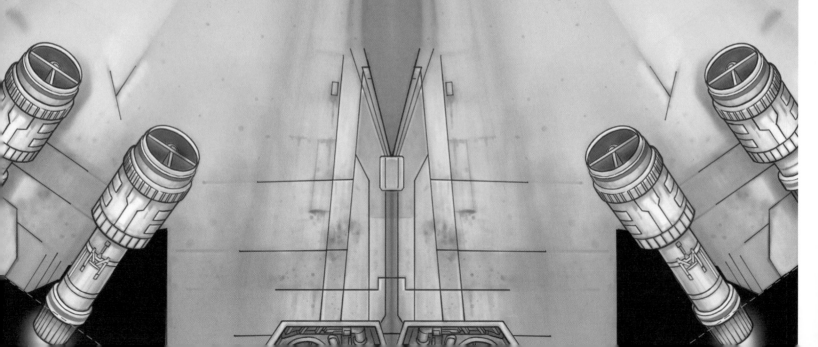

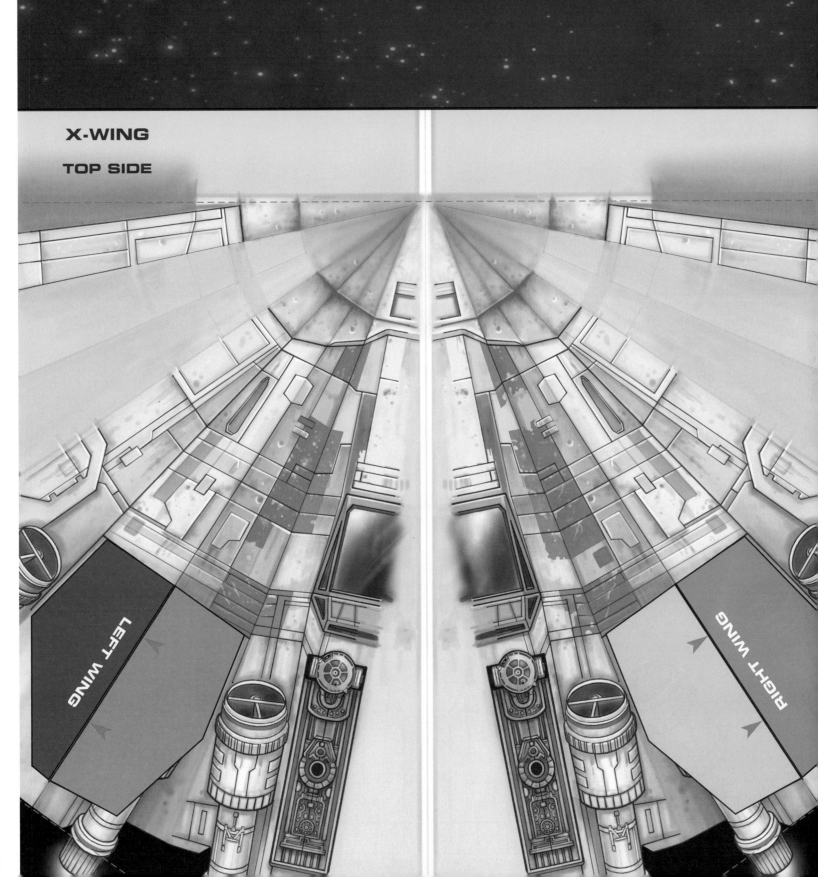

CUT OFF THIS SPACE

X-WING

TOP SIDE

LEFT WING

RIGHT WING

CUT OFF THIS SPACE

X-WING

UNDERSIDE

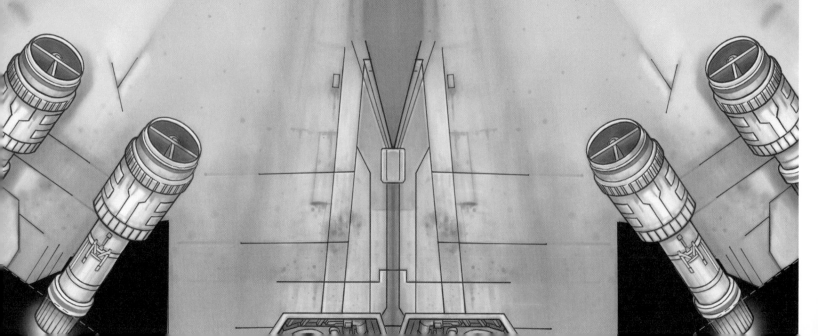

CUT OFF THIS SPACE

X-WING

TOP SIDE

LEFT WING

RIGHT WING

X-WING

UNDERSIDE

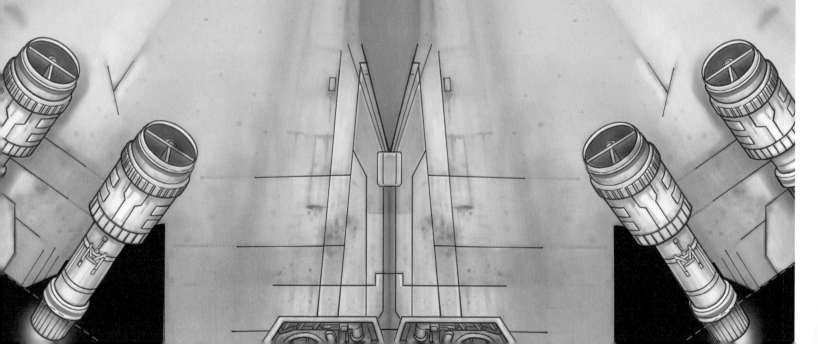

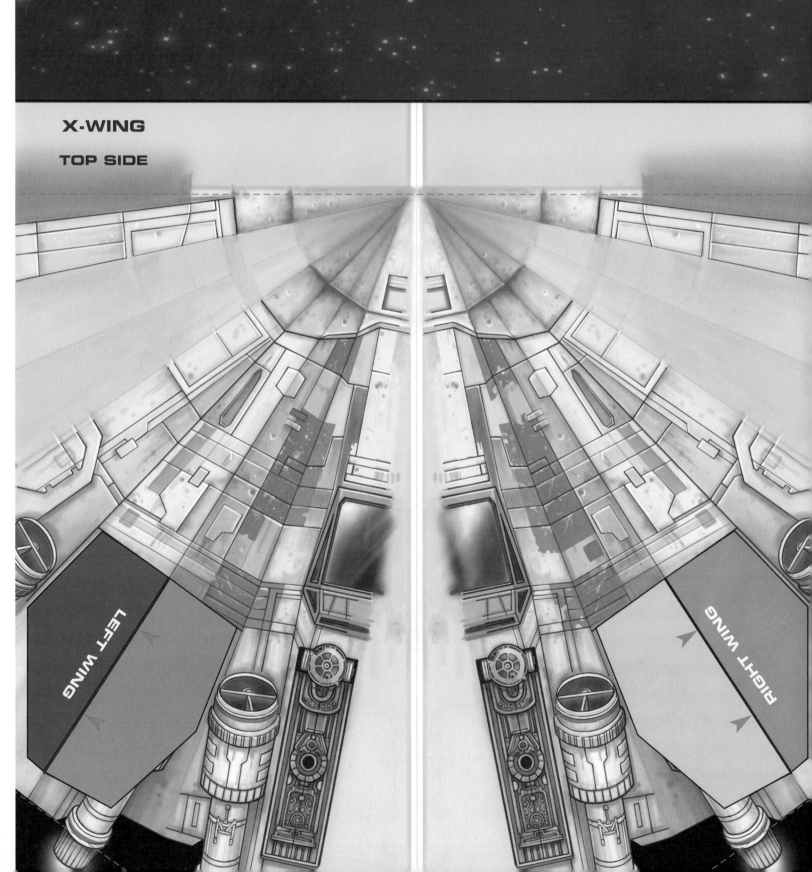

CUT OFF THIS SPACE

X-WING

TOP SIDE

LEFT WING

RIGHT WING

X-WING

UNDERSIDE

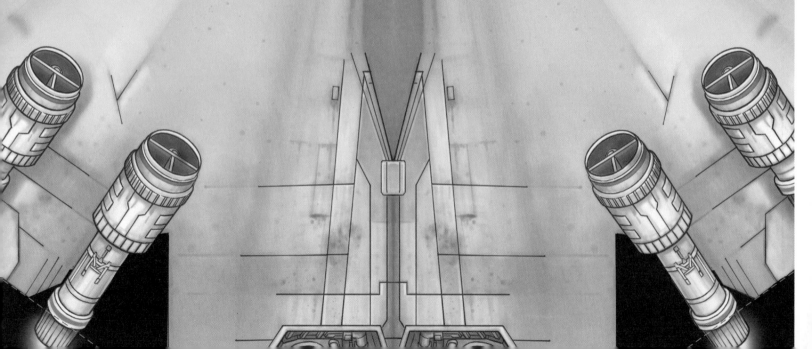

KLUTZ

STAR WARS
JEDI STARFIGHTER

KLUTZ

STAR WARS
MILLENNIUM FALCON

KLUTZ

STAR WARS
MILLENNIUM FALCON

KLUTZ

STAR WARS
JEDI STARFIGHTER

KLUTZ

KLUTZ

STAR WARS
TIE ADVANCED X1

STAR WARS
NABOO STARFIGHTER

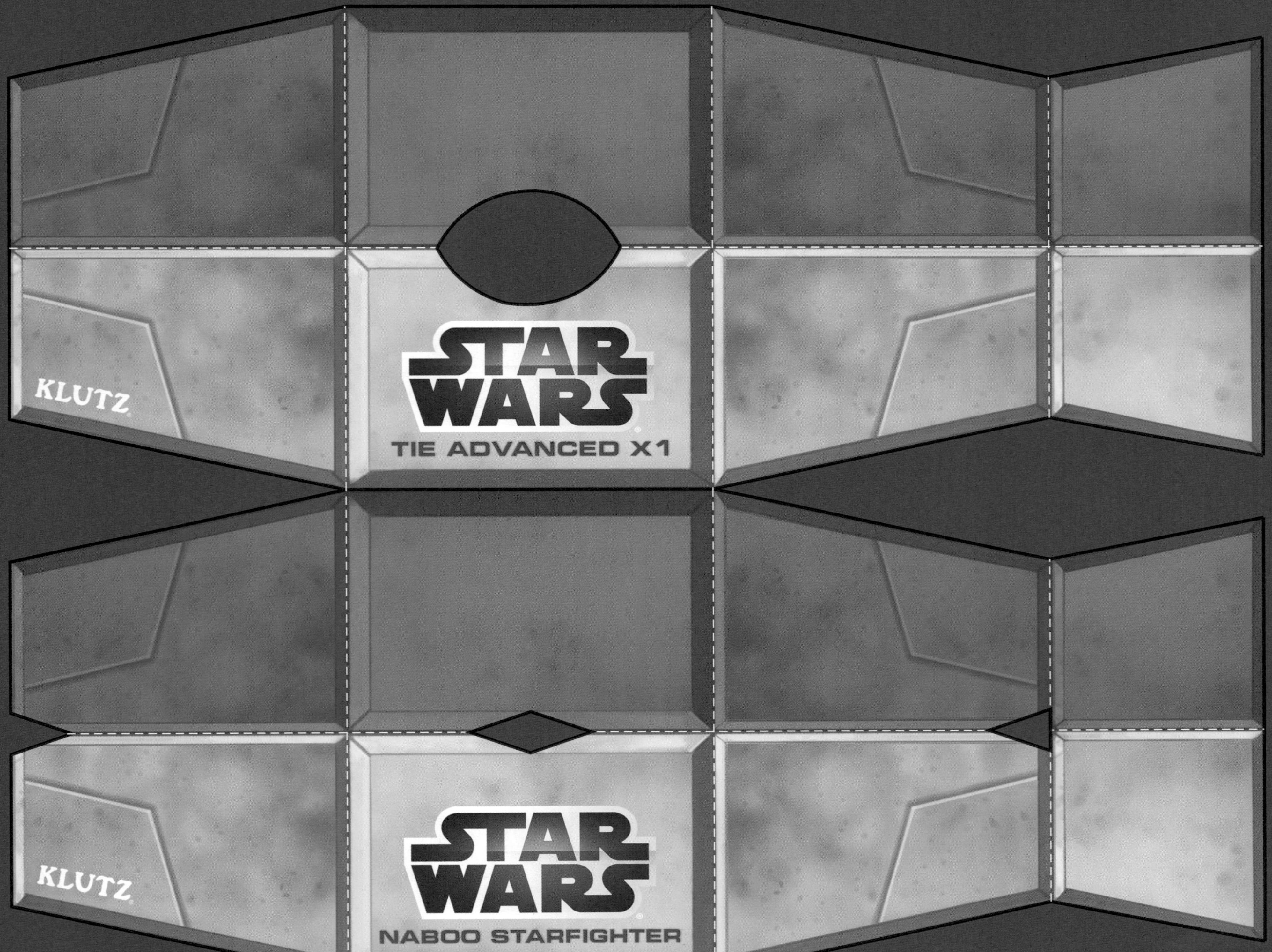

KLUTZ
STAR WARS
TIE ADVANCED X1
KLUTZ
STAR WARS
NABOO STARFIGHTER

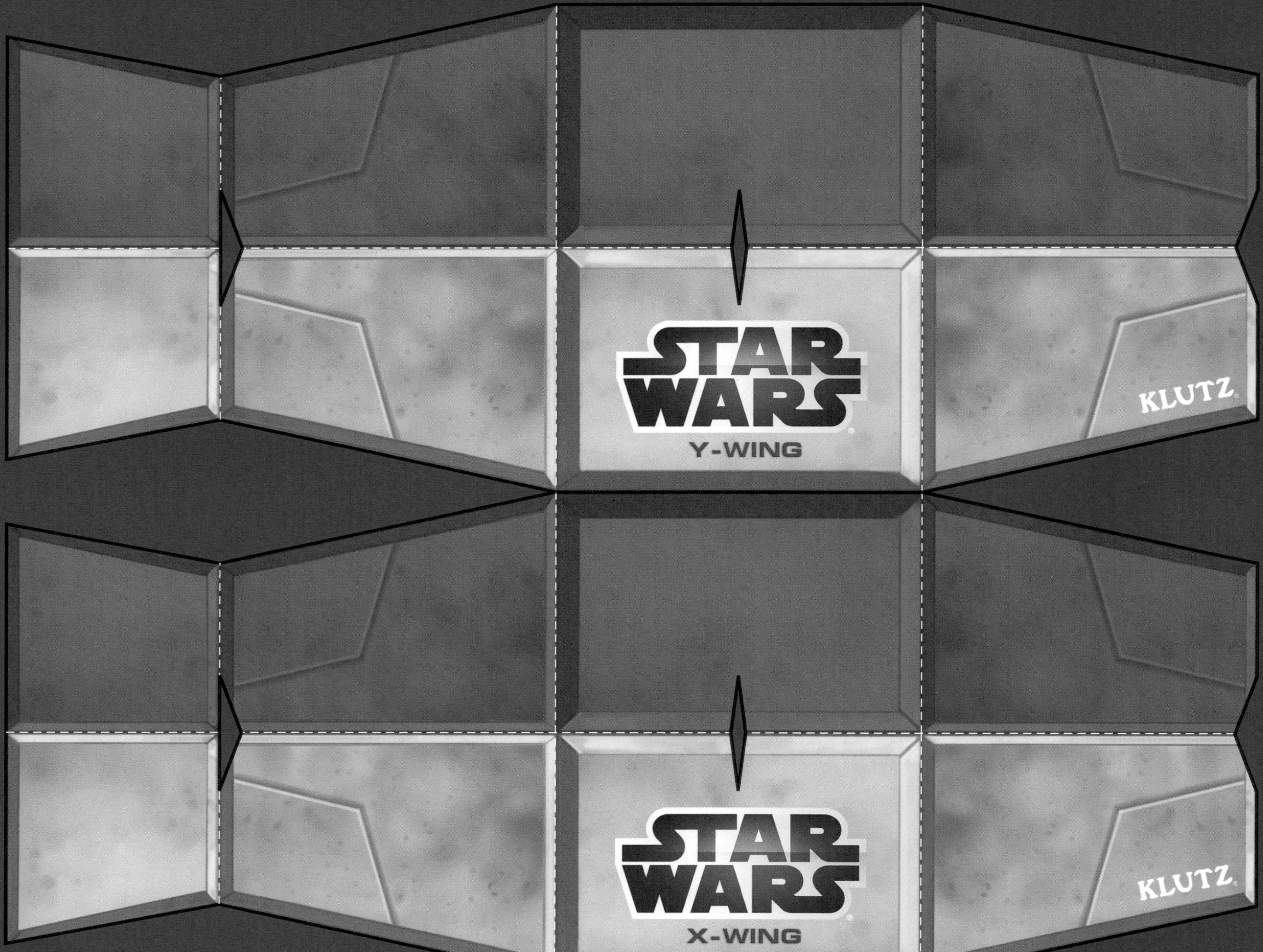
STAR WARS
Y-WING
KLUTZ
STAR WARS
X-WING
KLUTZ

KLUTZ

STAR WARS

X-WING

KLUTZ

STAR WARS

Y-WING